Previous Praise for Bob Servant

With My Head Held High

Bob Servant

First published in 2023 by
Winter & Simpson Ltd
16 Dunsinane Avenue
Dundee
DD2 3QT

The moral right of Neil Forsyth to be identified as the author of this work has
been asserted by him in accordance
with the Copyright, Designs and Patents Act 1988

isbn: 978-1-9161629-5-2

A catalogue record for this book is available
from the British Library

Printed and bound by Winter & Simpson Ltd, Dundee.

Contents

Introduction from Neil Forsyth

Three bewildering decades have passed since I first met Bob Servant. Over that time, I have known him as a window cleaner, a startlingly successful cheeseburger van operator and the author of books which I have been given the task of editing. This is his fifth book, and I am delighted it is his last.

Bob lives a life that is driven by whimsy and teeters on the edge of lunacy. Spending too long in his force field can be mentally expensive. Just look at his lifelong sidekick, Frank, a desperately troubled man who once turned to me and whispered 'Help me' while Bob was sleeping beside us on a bus.

Editing a book is a demanding task at the best of times. When it is conducted against a backdrop of flickering insanity it becomes truly torturous. To put together this compilation, I was instructed to return to our shared hometown of Dundee – Scotland's sunniest city that sits in honest contemplation by the River Tay. I was met by Bob at Dundee's gleaming train station. He took me on a tour of the city – sweeping up the Dundee Law hill to point out positions below where he had made particularly good jokes, zipping between the glory-drenched football stadiums, crawling respectfully past the city centre's Desperate Dan statue and then finally down into the riverside suburb of Broughty Ferry, Bob's personal fiefdom.

To see Bob walking the streets of Broughty Ferry is an astonishing sight. He liberally dispenses nods and winks to those he passes, whether they know him or not, and his hands are busy with shakes, pats and various tweaks which are greeted with delight by children and often extreme discomfort by adults. The sight of Bob roughhousing with an uncooperative traffic warden, who was on the verge of tears throughout, remains disappointingly fresh in my mind.

I spent a few weeks sorting through Bob's books – his email exchanges with internet scammers, his memoirs and his *Ask Bob* interactions with the public - then found myself on Bob's doorstep with the edited proof in my hands. Bob led me to his living room where he'd been relaxing with an indeterminate alcoholic cocktail and an episode of the *You've Been Framed* television show which I noticed, with alarm, was not being transmitted but was playing from VHS video. 'This clip is top three,' said Bob sincerely while we watched a man sit on a plastic bin at a family barbecue before the bin's lid gave way, sucking the man within it while screaming family members ran to his aid. 'Not of all time,' added Bob helpfully, 'just of that series.'

I wished Bob all the best for the future and said that, despite everything, working on his books had changed my life. He replied with the firm opinion that *You've Been Framed* clips involving people falling into water should be 'marked down' because they were 'as predictable as Christmas' and there was 'no real twist'. I shook Bob's hand and left him giggling quietly to himself, the mysterious cocktail close by and an endless stream of infantile entertainment flickering before him. In retrospect, I don't think I have ever seen him so happy.

Of all the reviews that Bob and I have had for the books, radio and TV, my favourite came from a Christian youth lifestyle magazine. 'These are the writings,' read the review, 'of a clearly deranged mind.' That came from someone who had spent perhaps an hour in Bob's company.

I have spent a lifetime.

Help me.

Neil Forsyth,
London, 2023.

A big 'Hello' from Bob Servant

Well, well, well. Here we are again, back in the book game for the very last time. In a great loss to Scottish literature I have decided to "hang up the biro" with this last, glorious compilation of my Greatest Hits. Over the years I have stormed the Dundee-based book charts with my laugh-an-hour emails, my autobiography (the best-selling autobiography in the wider Dundee area since the bible), and my genuinely useful Ask Bob guide to life.

It was a great misjudgement on my part to get the boy Forsyth in to edit my books. He is a dangerously unbalanced individual. I remember one day when he just totally lost it, saying how I'd ruined his life and all this. Well, if giving someone a chance in life is ruining their life then it's a very strange world we live in. I suppose I shouldn't be too hard on him. What do you expect from someone who's in their fifties and has never had a proper job[1]?

Like many, Forsyth made the critical mistake of thinking it's easy being me, but it's not. They see the big house and the extension and all my jumpers and so on and they think 'He's got it easier than Mandela'. But I don't. Because, like Mandela, my smile is just a frown in fancy dress and I'm under pressure. Terrible, terrible pressure.

When people see me in the street here in Broughty Ferry they all want a joke or a story. They want me to give them a wee slap or do something with my eyes they think is just for them. It's knackering and after a while it just gets too much. A lot of people say I'm just some sort of rogueish, twinkle-eyed, significantly muscled cowboy of The Old West. They think that's a criticism but it's not. Cowboys treated their horses like princesses and how many of us can honestly say that we've done the same? People who live in glass houses shouldn't criticise others when they can't even afford to live in proper houses.

When I finally shuffle off to the big disco in the sky, folk will say all sorts about me. They'll talk about me being a good man to have about the place, how I pretty much had the lot, and they'll talk at (almost) embarrassing length about my sexual energy. They'll say I left the punters howling with pleasure, that I sold Broughty Ferry to the world, and that I took on the boo boys and came out with my head held right up in the clouds.

---

[1] I am 45.

But more than anything, they'll say, "I remember Bob Servant. He was a genuine legend".

And they're right. I was. And am.

Your Servant,
Bob Servant
Broughty Ferry, 2023.

Foreword by Brian Cox

Getting involved with Bob Servant was the greatest mistake of my life.

Brian Cox
New York, 2023

Dear Bob,

I'd love to know more about your birth, which must have been a day of great Scottish celebration?

Chris Hoy, on my bike

* * * * *

Chris,

On the subject of my birth I will say only this. I have been genuinely scared three times in my life - the day I was born, the first time I used a Sodastream, and that time I thought I saw Fred West in Argos.

Bob

~~~~~~~~~~~~~~~

Dear Bob,

What was your time at school like? I'll be honest, I can't imagine it went well,

Toby Darcus, Scottish Borders

* * * * *

Toby,

It wasn't great. I went to school at Broughty Ferry Primary, slap bang next to the Mousetrap Factory which was for many years Dundee's largest employer until it's devastating closure in the 1980s[2]. Working in the Mousetrap Factory made the folk there completely immersed in violence and they took it out on us. Every morning a schoolkid would come in with a shiner or a dead leg. The Headmaster went to the factory to sort it out but the Manager there kicked him in the balls and after that our lesson times were switched so we didn't clash with the factory's shift changes, although even then I once got chased home by a woman who came off the nightshift and mistakenly detected sarcasm in my walk.

Yours in hope,

Bob

~~~~~~~~~~~~~~~

---

[2] The Dundee Courier, January 27th, 1985, "Mice Celebrate on Black Day for the City".

Bob,

I'm genuinely intrigued about your relationship with your parents, about whom we have only ever heard the odd snippet. Can you dig a little deeper?

Neal Devine, Sydney

* * * * *

Neal,

My Dad was a great guy. Apparently. We didn't see much of him. He said he was working on the North Sea oil rigs which sounds impressive but this was the 1950s and oil wasn't discovered in the North Sea until 1971[3].

For a while Mum and I clung to the theory that Dad was a visionary. Unfortunately for us he was a bigamist. We should have guessed. He'd head off for two weeks with his swimming trunks, a sieve and a copy of the Racing Post. No-one knew much about the oil game in those days but even as a youngster I remember thinking he must be pretty good at his job to get much oil with that gear. Dad's other family lived in Monifieth and I always respected him for that, not having them too close to home and rubbing me and Mum's faces in it. He told us all about them eventually, which was pretty tough and must have been one of the worst anniversaries he and Mum had ever had.

I remember the day my father died very well, largely because it was the day he died. I was sitting at my desk at school and spotted Mum in the corridor. She was there to tell me that Dad had, her words, kicked the bucket. Mum said the timing was awful because her Amateur Dramatics group were about to start a two-week run of Oliver Twist at the bowling club so I was to go and see Dad's other family and sort out the funeral. It was a lot of responsibility for a ten-year-old but Mum followed the Sir Alex Ferguson policy of 'if they're good enough they're old enough'. Plus, to be fair, Mum had just landed the plum part of Fagin which is a big ask for any actor, let alone a recently widowed woman.

The funeral was a strange old day. Mum had to go straight to a matinee so she was in her full Fagin costume which I was a bit uncomfortable with but I soon forgot about that when Dad's other wife arrived. I knew that her nickname was Bazookas and I presumed that she was maybe in the Territorial Army but when she walked into the church I saw that she most definitely wasn't in the Territorial Army and that wasn't why she was called Bazookas. I'll never forget the Minister's face when he came out to see the front row of me, Fagin and Bazookas. He must have thought he was part of

---

[3] The Dundee Courier. 3rd March, 1971. Dundee Lord Provost calls Aberdeen oil claim, "Laughable, Infantile and Unspeakably Arrogant".

a joke and to be fair he put on a decent show under the circumstances.

As a teenager, I met my best pal Frank, who would go on to be my sidekick in my many successes. He was a desperately troubled child, but offered loyalty that was in low supply elsewhere. When Dad died I said to Mum it was me and her against the world. She agreed that things weren't looking good for me but said it was unfair to drag her down with me. That was Mum in a nutshell – she had a real can-do attitude and after Dad died she concentrated on enjoying her life, including her attempt to break into the next level of showbusiness by emigrating to Forfar. As her taxi pulled away, Frank put his arm around my shoulder and said 'Don't worry Bob, you'll always have me'. I don't think I've ever felt as low in my life as when Frank said that. He really put the boot in,

Bob

– 1 –

Why Me? 1

From: Rose
To: Bob Servant
Subject: Why Me?

Hello dear,

My name is Rose. I am 24 years old and am residing in the refugee camp in Sudan as a result of the civil war in my country. Please listen to this important information. My late father was the managing director of a major Factory and he was the personal adviser to the former head of state before the rebels attacked our house and killed my mother and my father in cold blood. It was only me that is alive now and I managed to make my way to this camp.

When my father was alive he deposited money in one of the leading banks in Europe which he used my name as the next of kin. The amount in question is $9.3 (Nine Million three Hundred Thousand US Dollars). And i have contacted the bank so that i can have the money to start a new life but they requested that i should have a foreign partner as my representative due to my living status here. I know that you would be a proper person for this. I know already that I trust you. I need only your information.

Yours in love

Rose

From: Bob Servant
To: Rose
Subject: Why You Indeed, My Friend, Why You Indeed

Rose,

Thanks for writing. I'm going to say 'thanks but no thanks' to the money, as I'm worried that if I became a multi-millionaire I'd alienate my hardcore fans like what happened with Bruce Springsteen and Aneka Rice.

However, I am writing a book that is a collection of my exchanges with Internet cowboys like your good self. What happens is I have a wee chat with you and then we shake hands and go our separate ways. You wouldn't get any money from me but you'd see your name in print and it would be a funny story to tell your pals.

Let me know if you are available.

Thanks,
Bob

PS I attach a photo of the Dundee Waterstone's bestseller chart from last Christmas. As you'll see I'm at number 1 AND number 4. That's the kind of form you used to get from the Beatles for fuck's sake Rose.

From: Rose
To: Bob Servant
Subject: NO

OF COURSE I WILL NOT BE PART OF THAT. WHY WOULD I DO THIS? YOU THINK I HAVE TIME FOR THAT?

From: Bob Servant
To: Rose
Subject: That's Your Decision And I Will Respect It 100%

Fair enough. I'll try some others.

Dear Bob,
You have always had a fruitful and mutually respectful relationship
with women (your words), how did it start, and, more importantly, why
did it start?

Jack Whitehall, London

* * * * *

Jack,

Being highly attractive to women has been one of the great blessings
and curses of my life. It is a potent force that I have always wrestled
with, sometimes literally, and began when I was a young man in
Broughty Ferry's much-admired Sands Disco. Frank's dancing provided
my 'way in'. His dancing style is extremely violent, with a dependency
on kicks, karate chops and unnerving eye contact. When he was in full
flow, I would approach a nearby female, point at Frank and say 'I'll have
one of what he's having'. Saying 'I'll have one of what he's having' and
pointing at someone is a joke that's useful in many situations. The three
best times I've used the joke 'I'll have one of what he's having' were:
When David Icke was on Wogan, when Saddam Hussein invaded
Kuwait and when that guy got electrocuted by the cigarette machine in
Stewpot's Bar though I should say I didn't realise he was being
electrocuted when I made the joke[4].

Where does it come from, this spell I cast on the female folk? Could it
be my jumpers? I have, after all, what is generally regarded as one of the
top three jumper collections in the wider Dundee area. Or is it my eyes,
which twinkle more or less on demand, and even in their resting state
are like two small pools of water that women have been known to crash
cars whilst day-dreaming about diving into. Or is it, dare I say, my hair?
Thick, luxuriant and, more than anything, fun, my hair has been
known to cause females to lose control over their faculties and start to
follow me through the streets. More than once, I have turned round to
discover a gang of otherwise unconnected women have begun tailing
me through Broughty Ferry, transfixed by my hair and, dare I say, my
rear view[5].

[4] The Dundee Courier 18th May, 1994. "Broughty Ferry Businessman Apologises for
"Perfectly Timed but Ultimately Inappropriate Joke"
[5] The Dundee Courier, 19th August 2016. "I felt like the Pied Piper, Pun Intended", says
Broughty Ferry Businessman.

Other than hit myself in the face and, let's face it, groin with a hammer, there's not a huge amount I can do. I've just accepted small adjustments to my life to make things bearable. If I sit in public, I press my legs firmly together in case a woman is lurking nearby with binoculars and 'getting off' on the outline of my genitals through my corduroys. But it can become wearying. As I walk the streets of Broughty Ferry, my hands clasped behind my back, not in an arrogant way, more a "I've been there, and I've done that" manner, I am leered at by everyone from traffic warden-women to opportunistic female members of the clergy subjecting me to their 'elevator eyes'. According to Frank's records, 23% of our burger van customers are visibly aroused when ordering and that creeps towards 25% if I'm in my shorts.

To be honest, Jack, I've forgotten the question,

Bob

———~~~———

Dear Bob,

You strike me as no stranger to embarrassment, but what has been your most embarrassing moment?

Tommy Simpson, Monifieth

* * * * *

Tommy,

In 1983, I accidentally wore my jumper inside out to a bowling-club disco in Carnoustie. Sometimes I wonder if I ever recovered.

Yours in shame,

Bob

———~~~———

Dear Bob,

I live (God help me) in Cumbernauld. I like the odd pint but the pubs are bussing in bouncers from Glasgow. They're a scary bunch and I'm only a wee guy. How can I get over my fear and get back in the boozers where I belong? I think if I can crack this one my whole life will change for the better.

Wee Davie McD, Cumbernauld.

* * * * *

Davie,

The key with bouncers is to unsettle them by giving them a saucy, 'anything's possible' look, similar to those you used to get in the Carry On films and from fellow passengers in the early days of Intercity trains. That should work out just about fine.

Yours in hope,
Bob

Bob,

I'm almost scared to ask but do you, as man of advanced age, still embark on the kind of 'no rules' romantic adventures that you enjoyed as a younger man,

Jack Docherty, London

* * * * *

Dear Jack,

Yes, but with disastrous consequences. I was recently the victim of a coquettish bus conductress who pulled a classic 'kiss and tell' on me with the snakes at the Dundee Courier. Well, she was going to, so I just gave them a ring and got it over with.

Bob

WHAM BAM THANK YOU BURGER MAN!

'Servant Made Love All Night' says Bob Servant

Broughty Ferry businessman Bob Servant had a night of torrid passion on Saturday night, according to Broughty Ferry businessman Bob Servant. 'OK, fine,' said Servant this morning, after calling the Courier and asking for 'whoever does the filth'. 'Yes, you've got me,' he told us. 'I made love all night long.' Servant explained his partner in the endeavour was a 'bus conductress with a body built for sin, and for working as a bus conductress'.

'God-Given'

'I suppose you perverts won't rest until you get some more details,' continued Servant, unprompted. 'OK, fine. Just write, "Servant was like a wild animal but also surprisingly gentle and with the God-given ability to make just the right joke at just the right time." And call my body a treasure chest,' added Servant, who describes himself as a 'deeply private person'.

'Rock Bottom'

The bus conductress, who asked not to be named, told the Courier that she has 'finally hit rock bottom' and that maybe this is 'the wake-up call I need'. Servant described her comments as 'clearly tongue in cheek, pun intended'.

– 2 –

Bob the Oilman

From: Alan Thompson
To: Bob Servant
Subject: National Oil and Investment

Welcome to National Oil and Investment. I have come to you because I believe you are a man to be trusted and who will understand business. Tell no-one about this opportunity.

I am American man currently working here in Togo to drill and sell the best OIL. Due to over production at our plant in Togo we are in a lucky position to send you thousands of OIL free of charge. Because this is a secret deal with no tax to pay you will pay only the shipment fee and the goods will be yours to distribute in your own country. You can sell one barrel of OIL for $175. Shipment is $50,000 for 50,000 barrels of oil so you can see the profit to be made.

Looking forward to hearing from you soonest,

Mr Alan Thompson
Director
National Oil And Investment
Royal Plaza
Togo

From: Bob Servant
To: Alan Thompson
Subject: Oil Me Up

Alan,

The warmest greetings imaginable from Broughty Ferry, Dundee. Your email is one of the most exciting business opportunities that I have received by email from Western Africa this morning, and I can't offer much higher praise than that.

I would love to be in the oil game Alan. Being from Dundee we have to deal with the Aberdeen oil mob up the road and it is hard work. I don't mind people being rich, God knows I'm not short of a penny, but I like it when they wear their wealth with quiet dignity like His Majesty the King and Timmy Mallett. The Aberdeen mob are very much Novo Reach. They rub their oil money in your face (not in a saucy way) with their nice jumpers, matching shoes and high-end Ford Sierras.

This wee 'back door' into the oil business could be a chance not just for me, but for Dundee as a city to bounce back,

Your Servant,

Bob

From: Alan Thompson
To: Bob Servant
Subject: National Oil and Investment

Dear Bob Servant,
CONGRATULATIONS! You have been accepted as a new customer for us. Let us start the administration straight away so you can have your OIL soon enough. Now fill this form and send back for immediate processing.

FULL NAME:
CONTACT ADRESS:
PHONE NUMBER:
SEX:
AGE:
OCCUPATION:
COUNTRY:
STATE:
MATIRIAL:

Looking forward to hear from you soon

Bob you have the job! so please send the form.

Mr Alan Thompson
Director
National Oil and Investment
Royal Plaza
Togo

From: Bob Servant
To: Alan Thompson
Subject: Your Forthcoming Retirement

Alan,

I will have a good look at the form later today. It's great to be on board and cheers for appointing me to your job. I would like to thank you for all your work and wish you the best of luck for the future. As I will tell the lads at your retirement dinner, if I can be half the man you were, then I'll be happy! PS recognise these little guys?

All the best,
Mr Bob Servant
Director
National Oil and Investment
Royal Plaza
Togo

From: Alan Thompson
To: Bob Servant
Subject: National Oil and Investment

Bob,

That is my job. You do not have a title as you are only a customer. Please fill in the form. What is this picture?

Mr Alan Thompson
Director
National Oil and Investment
Royal Plaza
Togo

From: Bob Servant
To: Alan Thompson
Subject: Eh?

Alan,

I don't quite follow what you're saying about the job title, but we've got more important things to discuss which is what stories can I tell at your retirement dinner? Are you bringing the missus or can I be a bit risqué? A little birdie told me about the conference in Tenerife where a certain someone let his hair down quite spectacularly? There are whispers about you, a trolley dolly from Togo Airlines, a bath full of champers and a couple of dozen garden gnomes?

Kind Regards,
Mr Bob Servant
Director
National Oil and Investment
Royal Plaza, Togo

From: Alan Thompson
To: Bob Servant
Subject: National Oil and Investment

Bob,

You are not right in calling yourself this. It is my job, please stop. You are a customer. I am not going to retire why would I retire when I am young and there is so much money to be made? I have not been to Tenerife and don't know what this picture is about.

Send the form.

Mr Alan Thompson
Director
National Oil and Investment
Royal Plaza, Togo

From: Bob Servant
To: Alan Thompson
Subject: Make Your Mind Up

Alan,

Sorry you've completely lost me. One minute you're retiring and the next minute you're not. One minute you're boasting to anyone who'll listen about a night with a, your words, trolley dolly and the next you've never been to Tenerife? What's going on?

Kind Regards,
Mr Bob Servant
Director
National Oil and Investment
Royal Plaza
Togo

From: Alan Thompson
To: Bob Servant
Subject: National Oil and Investment

Bob,

I want to get on with the OIL and send it to your country for you to make a lot of money but do you see that you are calling yourself my job? I am the DIRECTOR you are the CUSTOMER. Do you understand? Do you not know business? I am NOT for retiring now. I have NOT been to Tenerife with anybody. STOP sending these pictures.

Mr Alan Thompson
Director
National Oil and Investment
Royal Plaza
Togo

From: Bob Servant
To: Alan Thompson
Subject: Take It Easy

Alan,

You want to keep the Tenerife stuff under wraps, I get it. But hold tight Alan, to accuse me of not knowing business is laughable. Where shall I begin? With the fact that in the late 1970s I had the longest window cleaning round in Western Europe,[6] or the fact that in the late 1980s I had fourteen cheeseburger vans going like a train 24 hours a day?[7] Or shall we talk about me being Broughty Ferry Businessman of The Year twenty-three years running?[8]

Kind Regards,
Mr Bob Servant
Alan Thompson's Best Pal and Hero
National Oil and Investment
Royal Plaza
Togo

From: Alan Thompson
To: Bob Servant
Subject: OK Fine Bob

Bob,

OK, let us just forget the job title situation as this does not matter. Yes we are now pals for sure and I did not mean to say you are not a businessman. You must be a famous businessman in your country if you have done all this. What matters Bob is your order being processed properly by us and you can get your OIL and make this big money. Please fill in the form and send back for immediate processing.

FULL NAME:
CONTACT ADRESS:
PHONE NUMBER:
SEX:
AGE:
OCCUPATION:
COUNTRY:
STATE:
MATIRIAL:

---

[6] See The Dundee Courier, 16 February 1978: 'The Pitter Patter of Lots of Ladders' ('Local man's windowcleaning round smashes 100-home barrier . . . "People said that was a glass ceiling," said Servant, "but I wash glass ceilings, that's the difference." ')
[7] See The Dundee Courier, various articles 1989–1991, such as 4 June 1990: 'Servant Wins Again' ('Broughty Ferry cheeseburger magnate Bob Servant last night celebrated the unveiling of his fourteenth van and launched a defiant tirade against other van owners involved in what many have dubbed "The Cheeseburger Wars" . . . "Why are people calling it the Cheeseburger Wars?" asked Servant, "if anything it's a massacre. This is our Dunkirk, and I'm Rommel."')
[8] See The Dundee Courier, 23 March, 1998. 'Dundee City Council Scraps Annual Award ('endemic corruption' . . . 'terrified judges' . . . 'silent phone calls'.)

From: Bob Servant
To: Alan Thompson
Subject: My Garage Awaits

Alan,

I accept your apology and I'm glad we're back on track. I have started sorting things out this end. Dundee is right on the River Tay so it shouldn't be a problem reversing in your oil tanker. Once it's arrived then it will be a case of getting the oil off and over to my house. I have a double garage with a much admired 'cantilever roof' so 50,000 barrels of oil should fit no bother at all. Can you please give me the name of the ship and also the name of the captain? I will fill in the form shortly, I'm just waiting for the right pencil to make itself known.

Thanks,
Bob

From: Alan Thompson
To: Bob Servant
Subject: Use Any Pencil

Dear Mr Bob

That is fine and we will deliver 50,000 barrels free of charge, you will simply pay the shipment. I will locate the name of the captain and his ship shortly Bob. Use any pencil or pen you have to hand it does not matter or best type it direct on the computer.

Mr Alan Thompson
Director NPC

From: Bob Servant
To: Alan Thompson
Subject: Here You Go

Alan,

No problem, info below, please send over the names of the ship and the captain.

Cheers Al,
Bob

FULL NAME: Bob Godzilla Servant
CONTACT ADRESS: Harbour View Road
PHONE NUMBER: No phone after I accidentally spent over £3,000 calling a phoneline that I believed was about wildlife[9]
SEX: Head to Toe 100% Male
AGE: 64
OCCUPATION: Businessman/Man About Town/A Good Guy To Have Around The Place

---

[9] See The Dundee Courier, 16 April 2010. 'Local Man Outraged by Porn Swindle' (' "Maybe I'm old fashioned," said Servant, "but to me a phone line calling itself Cougar Hunters should be about safaris" . . . Servant said he was "absolutely disgusted" by what he heard during a series of calls of up to an hour, made over a two-week period.')

COUNTRY: UK/Scotland/Dundee/Broughty Ferry
STATE: Excited
MATIRIAL: Eh?

From: Alan Thompson
To: Bob Servant
Subject: National Oil and Investment

Bob,

Thank you for your response. It is not all there but it is enough for now. OK, this is the captain's name and ship name

Captain Newman

Ship name: Edmund

You want 50,000 barrels of oil. Shipment is therefore $50,000. Payment should be sent immediately through Western Union.
BANK NAME: ECO BANK LOME TOGO
ADDRESS: ■■■■■■■■■■■■■■
A/C NAME. ■■■■■■■■■■■■■■
A/C NUMBER: ■■■■■■■■■■■■■■
SWIFT CODE: ■■■■■■■■■■■■■■
DESTINATION: LOME TOGO WEST AFRICA

As soon as you transfer the fee, send me the transfer slip for confirmation and immediate processing. Looking forward to hearing from you,

Mr Alan Thompson
Director

From: Bob Servant
To: Alan Thompson
Subject: The Dundee Courier

Alan,

Thanks for the account info and it's good of your friend to let you use his bank account for such a hefty wedge, you must trust that boy like there's no tomorrow.

Exciting news. A little birdie (not the same one) tipped off the Dundee Courier and they've done a bit of a splash on our link-up this morning, the article is attached. Can I just check what we are talking in terms of crew numbers? I will tell you right now that I will not have the crew staying in my gaff (known around Dundee as 'Bob's Palace'[10]). They can either stay at my neighbour Frank's house or if there's a few of them then I will sort something else out. But Captain Newman (I like him already!) will have his pick of the bedrooms

---

[10] I have never heard anyone ever refer to Bob's house as 'Bob's Palace' apart from Bob, despite his repeated attempts to have others do so. He once sent himself a letter addressed to Bob's Palace which resulted in a two-hour, highly-charged stand-off with his postman which left both men emotionally scarred.

at Bob's Palace, that's a promise. And if I break that promise, Alan, then you can break my arm.

With a fucking sledgehammer.

Bob

The Dundee Courier 25 January 2011

Dundee in Shock Oil News

Dundee celebrated today after a local businessman pledged to create an oil industry to rival neighbouring Aberdeen and bring untold riches to the city. Broughty Ferry entrepreneur Bob Servant, well known from the city's so-called Cheeseburger Wars, has struck a deal with African giants National Oil to 'flood' the city with cheap oil.

'This is the moment that Dundee has been waiting for,' said Servant today. 'Aberdeen has been a thorn in our side for too long and it's time for Dundee to grab a slice of the pie while it's still hot. I am doing this for the city and it's all gravy from here.'

Servant claims National Oil will begin sending vast quantities of oil in the next few weeks, delivering 50,000 barrels at a time in their famed supertanker, the SS *Edmund*, crewed by 200 men and captained by a man Servant describes as the 'world famous' Captain Newman. 'Captain Newman and his men are the best in the business,' says Servant. 'They could sail here blindfolded and, knowing Captain Newman as I do, he probably will.'

Servant says he will import enough oil for Dundee's own use as well as a surplus amount to sell to other Scottish cities. 'Because we're getting the stuff for peanuts, we can undercut Aberdeen to our heart's content,' said Servant. 'Edinburgh will be like a rat up a drainpipe, and I think we'll all enjoy seeing Glasgow come to us cap in hand. I'm in two minds on Perth, as I'm sure we all are.'

A spokesman for Dundee City Council hailed Servant as 'a visionary' while Tayside Police welcomed the news. 'Although usually the illicit importation and sale of oil would be a concern from the lawmaking point of view,' said a spokesman, 'in this case we'll be turning blind eyes all over the shop.'

'Some people are suggesting that I'm a hero,' Servant told *The Courier* last night. 'That's their decision. What I will say is this. I remember Liz Lynch being called a hero. And she came second. That's all I'm going to say. Hopefully you see what I'm saying. Liz Lynch came second. If you read between the lines you will see what I'm saying. She came second, but did I? That's what I am saying. Between the lines.'

From: Alan Thompson
To: Bob Servant
Subject: National Oil and Investment

Dear bob

I am glad to hear the news of DUNDEE In Shock Oil. we are very proud of you and we feel that the people will see you as a hero for sure. the director board of administrations has agree to shipped the oil for you as soon as poseble without any delay. we went to the bank to see if you have make the payment but not yet done. why? Bob kindly go to your BANK and make the payment today for immediate processing. You are correct. The Ship will be about 200 crew members,

Regards,
Mr Alan Thompson
MD

From: Bob Servant
To: Alan Thompson
Subject: Dundee's Going Mad for Captain Newman

Alan,

A lot of excitement here about Captain Newman. He's really got people talking. Men want to be him and women want to see him. Can I ask please, what are his main hobbies? And will he be happy talking about being a Captain and what other areas of conversation do you think he would want to talk about? The reason I ask is that I know from bitter experience how difficult captains can be.

In 1983 I bumped into Dundee United's league winning captain Paul Hegarty in Safeways. He was standing next to the tinned fish aisle and quick as a flash I said,

'Afternoon skipper, buying some kippers?'

It was a decent joke, not the best I've ever told (not even the best I've ever told in the tinned fish aisle) but the way he looked at me Alan, my God, it could have frozen the sun. Captains are unpredictable and sometimes they don't like the same jokes as normal people. So I need to tread carefully with Captain Newman.

Finally, please send me the names of the 200 crew members which I presume you'll have close to hand in a file. It's so I can book their hostel rooms. Nicknames are fine.

Bob

From: Alan Thompson
To: Bob Servant
Subject: National Oil and Investment

Dear bob,

Well Captain Newman likes all kinds of jokes and he likes everything such as smoke and drink. I have spoken to him and he says this is a great honour to stay with you at Bob's Palace.

Here are your crew names for the hotel.

AARON, ABA, ABAY, ABBA, ABBOTT, ABBY, ABCDE, ABDIEL, ABDUKRAHMAN, ABDULKAREEM ABDULLAH, ABDULRAHMAN, ABE, ABEDNEGO, ABEEKU, ABEL, ABELARD, ABHAY, ABIE, ABIYRAM, ABNER, ABRAHAM, ABRAM, ABSOLOM, ABU, ACE, ACHAVA, ACHILLES, ACOOSE, ACOTAS, ACTON, ADAHY, ADAIR, ADAM, ADAN, ADARSH, ADDAE, ADDISON, ADE, ADEBEN ADELIO, ADEM, ADEN, ADIEL, ADISH[11]

Now Bob it is time to send the payment

Alan

From: Bob Servant
To: Alan Thompson
Subject: The Names

Alan,

Thanks so much for those 200 names. At first I thought I could see some sort of pattern with them but maybe I'm imagining it. You also left a link at the bottom of your email to a website called 'Baby Names' so I presume you and Mrs Thompson are expecting a little one. Congratulations, I hope he or she grows up to respect you as much as I do.

For 200 people I think it would be best to stick them in the Sleep Tight and Don't Fight Hostel in Lochee.[12] I will get the rooms booked up now. I would estimate that the booking will also cost around $50,000 so shall we just call it level on the money?

Finally, a few last questions on Captain Newman.
You said he likes to drink, what is his favourite drink?
He's obviously not shy of a party, is he a big fan of women (in Dundee we call them skirt, which they like a lot)?
Does he sing any songs at parties?
How long has he been at sea?
He sounds like a mad dog, is he a mad dog?

Thanks,
Bob

---

[11] I have edited out the rest of these 200 names, which continue in a predictable vein.
[12] See www.tripadvisor.com Review entitled 'To Hell And Back' ('anarchy' . . . 'keen sense of danger' . . . 'kung-fu kick . . . from the receptionist')

From: Alan Thompson
To: Bob Servant
Subject: National Oil and Investment

Bob,

Answers below but that is it now, you must send the payment for the OIL shipment. We will pay for the hostel ourselves because that is the way we do business here. Captain Newman and I are both waiting. Come on Bob, send this payment and you will make more money than you will understand.

You said he likes to drink, what is his favourite drink? . . . RUM

He's obviously not shy of a party, is he a big fan of women (in Dundee we call them skirt, which they like a lot)? . . . YES IF GOOD

Does he sing any songs at parties? . . . NO

How long has he been at sea? . . . 15 YEARS

He sounds like a mad dog, is he a mad dog? . . . OK YES.

From: Bob Servant
To: Alan Thompson
Subject: Game Over

Alan,

Big, big problems my end. I have been updating the folk here in Dundee about Captain Newman and it's gone down like a lead balloon. The irony is that the more that I hear about Captain Newman the more I like and respect him, but for others it seems it's quite the opposite. It's bad news all round I'm afraid. I tried a bit of 'firefighting' but unfortunately The Courier got hold of the story and that's our goose cooked.

The article's attached, there's no way back from this unfortunately. When the folk round here turn on you, it's time to walk away, but when the Dundee Skirt Protection League get on your tail, then it's time to run for the hills.

All the best for the future, and please pass on my regards to Captain Newman and the crew. I can't believe I will never meet them in the flesh.

Your Servant,
Bob Servant

The Dundee Courier 30 January 2011

Dundee Rejects 'Mad Dog' Captain

Dundee closed ranks today against the proposed arrival in the city of an oil tanker captained by a man described by his own company representative as a 'mad dog'.

Captain Newman, of the SS *Edmund*, was supposed to be delivering the oil that would kick-start an oil industry in Dundee to rival that of Aberdeen. The news of the ship's impending arrival provoked local celebrations earlier this week but, as news emerged yesterday of Captain Newman's true character, Dundee awoke this morning with a sour taste in its mouth.

It was National Oil's Scottish representative Bob Servant whose comments at a media briefing this morning provoked panic.

'He's a mad dog,' shrugged Servant. 'That's what they call him. Look, the guy has been at sea for fifteen years and he's seen the lot – pirates, tidal waves, Fife. Who wouldn't lose their mind? But, yes, he's a loose cannon. I can't deny that. We deal in honesty at National Oil.'

'First and foremost he loves skirt,' continued Servant. 'He's skirt mad and he always has been. When I say "Lock up your daughters when Captain Newman is about" I really do mean "Lock up your daughters when Captain Newman is about" because otherwise absolutely anything can happen.'

'He also loves a drink,' added Servant, 'especially rum which he will do almost anything to get his hands on. And he smokes like a chimney, so good luck to anyone trying to enforce the smoking ban when the skipper's about! He'd rip their head off and throw away the key.'

Servant's words were greeted with dismay and fear by the authorities. A spokesman for Dundee City Council said 'National Oil are no longer welcome in the city,' while Tayside Police released a statement that Newman would be 'arrested on the spot' if he arrives in Dundee. A spokeswoman for the Dundee Skirt Protection League said they would be protesting outside Servant's humble Broughty Ferry home this weekend if the deal wasn't cancelled.

From: Alan Thompson
To: Bob Servant
Subject: Ignore what they are saying

Bob,

Forget all these troubles and SEND THE PAYMENT. STRAIGHT AWAY

Alan

NO REPLY

Bob,
My mother-in-law's perfume is extremely strong. I think it's some
eighties concoction called 'Lust' or 'Hot Spice' or suchlike. What can I
do?

'Overpowered', Brighton

* * * * *

My friend,

When two skunks meet each other on a mountain path they spray each
other down and continue on their way. In much the same way, you
need to start wearing the same scent as your mother-in-law. Over time,
you will become immune to the smell and diminish her power as a
result. The only slight downside is that there is a fairly high chance your
father-in-law will become sexually attracted to you. If this happens then
you have to 'turn him off'. The easiest way is to find out which of your
mother-in-law's dresses he finds the least attractive and wear it
whenever in his company. That should cool his misplaced passions and
allow you to retain every possible shred of dignity,

Yours,
Bob

Bob,
You're obviously an inspiration to many, but who
is your inspiration?

Yours with deepest respect,
Gordon Smart, Kinross

* * * * *

Gordon,
Churchill, Mandela, Humperdinck.

Yours in hope,
Bob

Bob,
As a Scotsman recently moved to London, I've been absolutely
flummoxed by the way people greet each other at lunches and work
drinks. Single kiss, double kiss, hugs. What are the rules? It's like
the Wild West. I met someone the other day and I was all over the
place, I pretty much ended up putting her in a headlock. Help.

Paul Instrell, Ealing

* * * * *

Paul,
This sounds horrific and you have my full sympathies. I suggest you
adopt the Dundee rules, which are very clear. Handshakes (no eye
contact) for men, thumbs-ups (brief eye contact) for women.

Yours in hope,
Bob

Dear Bob,

I like to think I am a 'good catch' but when I'm around women I go to
pieces, like a box of broken biscuits.

Please help,

'On the Shelf', Carnoustie

* * * * *

Hello pal,

Sorry to hear that, and you're in luck. The one benefit of the incessant
female attention I receive is that I have gained a deep understanding of
women, which I will kindly share for the greater good,

Yours in Hope,

Bob

"Guide to Women"
Bob Servant

1. How to Calm An Angry Woman.

The easiest way to calm an angry woman is to place your finger on her lips and say, 'You are being utterly ridiculous.' The vast majority of women will instantly fall silent, apologise profusely and your Hell will soon be over.

2. How to Compliment a Woman.

There are many ways to compliment a woman. You can say that you largely like her jumper, that she has a terrific walk, that her make up doesn't look overly clownish, or, my favourite, simply caress her hair and say "Dare I say, Timotei?"

3. How to Resolve Conflict with a Woman Before She Pulls a Hiroshima.

My friend Tommy Peanuts had a wonderful piece of advice - "Always go to bed on an argument". No matter what time of day Tommy's wife had a go at him, Tommy would simply pop on his pyjamas and go to bed. It greatly cut down the amount of arguing and worked wonders for Tommy's complexion. Unfortunately, his wife left him for a fun-loving electrician and Tommy now lives in a hostel, where sleeping conditions are a wee bit trickier.

4. When To Tell A Woman That Her Hair Looks Ridiculous.

The best time to tell a woman that you think her hair looks ridiculous is in the immediate aftermath of a car accident. If that option isn't available then take the sting out of the situation by phoning her work and asking a colleague to pass on the message, or simply whisper constructive criticism of her hair just before she falls asleep.

– 3 –

Alexandra, Bob and Champion

From: Alexandra
To: Bob Servant
Subject: Hello!

Hello, my new friend! My name is Alexandra, 25 years old. I live in Russia and want to get acquainted with man from other country. Be not surprised to my letter. I have learned your address in agency of international acquaintances. I do not know, like you my photo or not? At once I want to say I do not search the relation for games. I want to find the husband! I shall expect answer with impatience!

Best wishes, Alexandra

P.S. Please, send to me your photo.

From: Bob Servant
To: Alexandra
Subject: By Christ You Could Take Someone's Eyes Out With Them

Alexandra,

How are you? What a fantastic photo. It made my legs feel like raw mince. How is life in Russia?

Your Servant,
Bob Servant

From: Alexandra
To: Bob Servant
Subject: Hello!

Dear Bob!

I am very glad that you have answered my letter! It is a pity, that you have not sent me the photo. It is a problem? I live in city Vladivostok. Probably, you think me beautiful and think, that at me it is a lot of admirers. Yes, I shall not begin to deny it. But I do not like the Russian men, their attitude to women. I want to love and be loved. Unfortunately, I have not found it in the country. I am gentle women but I am a tiger when I am in love!

Alexandra

From: Bob Servant
To: Alexandra
Subject: YOU LIKE THE TIGER? I LIKE THE LION!

Alex,

I can certainly sympathise with anyone who has a love of large cats, being a Grade A lion nut myself.

When I am in love, I think I most resemble a seagull, with an enormous wingspan, which I don't demonstrate in an arrogant way, only deploying when genuinely needed in high winds.

Bob

From: Alexandra
To: Bob Servant
Subject: OK

I do not understand fully you. It seems to me, that you are frivolous a man. You would like to play only? Where is your photo? What can you offer me to make me love you?

From: Bob Servant
To: Alexandra
Subject: Chill out

Alexandra,

I apologise, let me give you a little more info. I am a cheeseburger van Svengali from Broughty Ferry, Dundee. There is no point denying that I have done very, very well from the cheeseburger game. I have attached a photo of myself from a recent fishing trip[13]. What do you think? About me, not the fish!!

Bob

From: Alexandra
To: Bob Servant
Subject: A question

The Fish is simply magnificent!:) And it is possible an immodest question? How old are you?

From: Bob Servant
To: Alexandra
Subject: IT WAS A GREAT FISH AND VERY TASTY TOO!

Alexandra,

Thank you for your kind words. That fish nearly ripped my bloody arms out. I am 64 years old, but I am as fit as a fiddle.

Bob

---

[13] This man is not Bob Servant. I have no idea who he is, but the fish looks like a mirror carp.

From: Alexandra
To: Bob Servant
Subject: Age

It is very a pity, Rob, but it seems that we are not created for one another... To me 23 years, you – 64 years. What prospects of our relations? Let's look at things really. What can you offer me? Your humour?

From: Bob Servant
To: Alexandra
Subject: It's your call of course but I do genuinely like you!

Alexandra,

I see you chose to call me Rob there. I can only hope that this was a one-off. I remember Tommy Peanuts telling me that Bob Wilson beat a jockey half to death live on Grandstand in the early 1980s after the jockey called him Rob[14] and I have to admit that it makes me just as mad. It's Bob or nothing Alexandra, and that's that. You are a frank woman and that is one of the things that I love about you.

My success has left me a man of leisure here in Broughty Ferry. I buy supermarket Finest meals, use pound notes to blow my nose, and my postie was recently hospitalised due to the length of my drive. It's your call Alexandra.

Bob

From: Alexandra
To: Bob Servant
Subject: Hello!

Dear Bob, never Rob!

It was very pleasant to receive from you these answers! You very interesting! At leisure I like to look cinema. I like film " Forrest Gump " where a leading role has played Tom Hanks. It is very good film, where many various philosophical ideas and ideas. I also very much like to dance. I could learn to dance you!

If you want to write to me the letter, my full post address: ■■■■■ ■■■■■■■■■ ■■■■■■■■■ Vladivostok, Russian Federation. I think that a meeting is necessary for us! We already can name each other good friends. I am right? I like your sense of humour. I tell my good friends about you,

Can we meet New Year together? We shall make a mad act? I can arrive to you. If the idea has liked – answer quickly and we shall discuss details. I have the passport and good friends in a travel company, which can issue the visa but there is a banal problem. Money. I did not plan trip now. That is I openly speak,

---

[14] There is no record of the former international goalkeeper turned television presenter Bob Wilson ever having physically attacked a jockey, either on or off air.

that I have no financial opportunity. If you have an opportunity to help me with money then our meeting will be a reality and we can meet New Year together!

Your Alex

From: Bob Servant
To: Alexandra
Subject: OPPORTUNITY AT STEWPOT'S

Alex,

I am delighted you want to come here for New Year. You are a strong, exciting woman who knows when to stand up for herself. A scrappy, no rules fighter, like Rocky Balboa or Richard Madeley.

I am a man of means, there is absolutely no doubt about that, but I worry you'll be bored with nothing to do so I was thinking you could take a part-time job? Stewpot's Bar has a note up for a lunch waitress?

Bob

From: Alexandra
To: Bob Servant
Subject: Job is not problem

My Darling Bob!

I agree to work some time as the waitress. It would be amusing:) It is valid, it will help me to earn money and in training to English, you are right. You to me are very interesting and want to see you now! But to issue the visa for such short time, additional financial assets will be necessary. It is necessary for me of 1000 euros that the visa was ready this week. I want to pay for air tickets itself. But money for the visa are necessary already tomorrow!

Yours Alex.

From: Bob Servant
To: Alexandra
Subject: Issues

Alex,

Just received the job application from Stewpot's Bar. Send me back the answers as soon as possible please.

WHY DO YOU WANT TO WORK IN STEWPOT'S?
WHAT DO YOU THINK YOUR BEST SKILLS ARE?
DO YOU PROMISE NOT TO CARVE CARROTS INTO NOBS?
ARE YOU HONEST?

All the best,
Bob

From: Alexandra
To: Bob Servant
Subject: My Answers for Terry

Dear Bob!

I have just received the letter and I answer your questions.

WHY DO YOU WANT TO WORK IN STEWPOT'S?
I want to work during my trip to Bob to not be to a burden and consequently, that I like to work, communicate with people. I do not like to idle.

WHAT DO YOU THINK YOUR BEST SKILLS ARE?
I specialize on Russian cuisine more. But I can prepare the Italian and Mexican cuisine also.

DO YOU PROMISE NOT TO CARVE CARROTS INTO NOBS?
:)))) Certainly. But suddenly it clients will want? For me desire of the client – the law:)))

ARE YOU HONEST?
For all time of the life I tried to communicate with people fairly and to deceive nobody. For me the bitter truth is always better than sweet lie. Yes, I am fair with you 100%.

So, I hope, that have answered all your questions. Now answer you and it is maximum fast. When you can send me 1000 euros for the visa? And a special photo too for you Bob,

1. Name of the addressee: Alexandra
2. Surname of the addressee: Dadashov
3. City and country of the addressee: Vladivostok, Russia

I hope, that you can make it in the nearest hour because our banks work only up to 3 PM.
Alex

From: Bob Servant
To: Alexandra
Subject: WHAT A CLEVER PHOTO!

Hello Alex,

What a clever photo! At first I thought it was just you blowing old Bob a kiss and then I looked at the computer screen and there was old Bob himself! Great stuff. A nice idea, well executed. Needless to say, you have secured the lunchtime waitress position.

I will be going to the bank soon to send your money, but in the meantime, I have bought something that I think you will like. I will give you a clue. You need to feed it. Can you guess?

Bob

From: Alexandra
To: Bob Servant
Subject: Hello

Bob!

I did not want to lose good relations with my friends in a travel company. I have already informed you, how you can help me. You can have a way to any branch Western Union. I have made all for this purpose. If you will not help me, I shall be compelled to give in parts 1300 euro to my friends within several months. I think now that you play with me?

Yours Alex

From: Bob Servant
To: Alexandra
Subject: Lunatic

Alex,

What kind of lunatic would spend all this time emailing you if they were not serious?

Bob

From: Alexandra
To: Bob Servant
Subject: I am sorry

My dear Bob!

I am sorry for behaviour. I am very tired... I very much want to be with you. You should understand, that for me it is very difficult to accept again the man. But you have very much liked me, I do not hide it. And now I shall be very glad, if our meeting with you will take place. I wait for concrete actions. I am very much intrigued with this surprise which you have prepared me?
I am ready to see my present:))

From: Bob Servant
To: Alexandra
Subject: HERE WE GO!
HE'S CALLED CHAMPION!

From: Alexandra
To: Bob Servant
Subject: I like it

My dear Bob!

This is definitely a surprise OK. Your gift is very originally. Still anybody similar in life did not give anything to me. Now about our affairs. I very much hope, that today you will make that for a long time promised me . . . to Western Union! I expect your answer...

Alex

From: Bob Servant
To: Alexandra
Subject: NOT LONG NOW!

Alex,

I am so excited that you like your present. I was going to Carnoustie on the bus the other day when I spotted Champion in a field. Every household in Carnoustie owns at least one ostrich[15] but for some reason the farmer hadn't shifted Champion. Tomorrow I'm going to have a couple of liveners at Stewpot's Bar, then nip up to Carnoustie on the bus and pick up Champion, then I'll come back here, tie him up in the garden and race round to the Post Office to send the cash. Any idea what I should feed Champion? Would he eat chips?

Bob

---

[15] True

From: Alexandra
To: Bob Servant
Subject: Let us resolve this today now

Send the money as the most important part of your travels tomorrow. Certainly, I very much wait happily for our meeting. It will be better, if to my arrival the Champion will be little bit hungry then I could feed him:) Chips? He loves chips? I never saw ostriches earlier, it is very interesting to me:))

Now I wait from you for the information on a remittance that I could continue the preparation to be with you and Champion.

Alex

From: Bob Servant
To: Alexandra
Subject: A rollercoaster of a day

Alex,

An unforgettable day. I went along to Stewpot's first thing and told all the boys I was off to pick up an ostrich for my Russian girlfriend and they all laughed along in pride for what I have achieved. So it was a good atmosphere and then they started saying that Russian men can drink a bottle of vodka straight and if I couldn't do that then you would leave me. I'm a drinker Alex, I've never hidden that from you but I have two Achilles heels. The first is strong women and the second is vodka. In both case, they can send me a little blurry.

I got off the bus fine though did fall, with dignity, into a hedge. I didn't have a lead so took off my jumper and stuck it over Champion's head and used a sleeve to lead him to the bus stop. The farmer appeared and went absolutely berserk. He was saying stuff like, 'what are you doing?' and 'you're a fucking basket case and I'm going to call the police'.

I kept my head held high until the bus came but the driver, as they often do, lacked ambition and said there was no way I could bring an ostrich on the bus. I said to just charge him half fare but then the other people on the bus started getting involved (even though it was none of their business) and were all screaming and stuff.

Of course, that set Champion off, lashing out with his feet (hooves?) and pecking away. He lifted a woman's bunnet clean off and caught a man with a moustache an absolute beauty on the side of the head. 'That's one peck on the cheek you didn't ask for!' I said, in an admirable attempt to lighten the mood but the guy was one of those "I'll do the jokes" types.

The police turned up so I went to have a "no strings" chat with them but tripped and went into what I believe was a second hedge but might have been a return journey to the first. I don't remember much after that. I shouted 'See you later Champion, you can keep the jumper' but he didn't reply.

The police say I might get hit with a hefty fine for cruelty, so I'll need that money I was going to use for your visa. I'm sorry about Champion and while it was a fun suggestion of yours to get hold of an ostrich, I think one of us has to be the "grown up" here, and I'm afraid I don't think it's safe to have a family pet that could go off the handle like that.

All is not lost! I bought a dog on the way home. Photo attached.

All my love and genuine respect,

Bob.

From: Alexandra
To: Bob Servant
Subject: Re: a rollercoaster of a day

Fuck you! To me has bothered to read your delirium

Bob,

What is your evening routine? I can imagine things can get pretty lively when the curtains are drawn?

Peter Silverstone, Newcastle

* * * * *

Pete,

People think that every night round mine is the last Days of Rome material and, hands up (literally), it often is. But by and large it's a case of getting home, popping off the daytime corduroys, popping on the evening corduroys, and settling down with a mug of room temperature Midori in front of my ten-inch flatscreen. And they said I'd never make it!

Yours in hope,
Bob

Dear Bob,

Perhaps you might offer advice on a delicate matter. Having been married for 40-odd years, I'm beginning to find my wife's lack of enthusiasm in the boudoir department something of a problem. Any advice in rekindling a flame from the dying embers of our once-passionate love life would be appreciated. It goes without saying that since I don't want my small-but-loyal army of elderly fans tittering amongst themselves at Taggart conventions, perhaps in the book you can refer to me using a nickname.

Sincerely,
Alex 'A Nickname' Norton, Languedoc, France

* * * * *

Alex,

You're in luck. As I became, and I hate this phrase, a Ladies Man of Unbelievable Repute, I realised that I should not be the only one to gain from the experience. I poured my knowledge of what makes women tick into my ongoing collection of romantic fiction, which remains available from under the counters of all good Broughty Ferry newsagents.

I enclose a free extract for you now, which should do the trick at your end for you and your wife. However, do not let her read it if she is prone to hot flushes or she will be at genuine risk of self-combustion,

Yours,
Bob

Chapter One

A Great Night For the Stags!

"Oh it's yourself", said Lord Dundee as he opened the door. Lord Dundee was a handsome bastard of a man. Great big muscles and nice hair and a good smile and teeth and big muscles. He opened the door and in walked a very nice woman indeed. "Hello Lord Dundee, my name is Victoria Magnolia" said the woman.

She was a fantastic woman in both looks, walk and general vibe. She had lovely long blonde hair like the sun and her eyes made Lord Dundee feel like his legs had turned to mince.

"Well, well, well Victoria Magnolia", said Lord Dundee, laughing in a way that showed he was not under any pressure whatsoever. "Well, well, well". "Oh Lord Dundee", said Lady Magnolia who was also a Lady but not because she was married to Lord Dundee because she wasn't. His wife had died in the War and her husband Lord Magnolia was just a wee guy and didn't have any legs because of the War, but he was wee anyway even despite the legs situation and hardly a patch on Lord Dundee who had long legs but in complete mathematical proportion to the rest of his excellent body.

"Well, well, well", said Lord Dundee and behind him was all the heads of the stags that he'd killed when he was hunting up in the Highlands around Inverness and also in other parts of the Highlands. "You're a sight for sore eyes Victoria Magnolia, I'll tell you that for free". Victoria Magnolia was a sight for sore eyes all right. She was bloody gorgeous and she didn't take herself seriously but that's not to say she was always telling jokes. She laughed at Lord Dundee, certainly not making fun of him but in admiration and put her hand over her mouth as if to say "Whoops!"

"Well, well, well", said Lord Dundee. And then he said "Are you looking for this" and he took off his gloves and hung them on the head of one of the stags he had shot, and then he was ready and Victoria Magnolia thought "Oh oh".

Dear Bob,

As a fellow jumper fan, would you agree with me that a big part of life is making sure you have a really nice jumper?

Alex Van Klaveren, Lisbon

* * * * *

Dear Sandy,

Absolutely. Good jumpers are like good dreams, you don't know where they come from and you want to tell your postie all about them. They say by the time he's 64, a man has the jumper he deserves, and my God I have proved that in spades.

Yours in hope,
Bob

Bob,

As a Scottish telly star, Bob, can you tell me if that stratospheric level of fame is all it's cracked up to be? Is fame worth it Bob, or are there more important things in life?

Kevin Thomson, Brighton

* * * * *

Kevin,

Yes, the television documentary sent me into the big leagues, but I hardly came out unscathed. What they did to me was frankly outrageous, and when I was good enough to try to help they ignored me. Fame costs, there's no doubt about that one.

Yours in anger,
Bob

Bob Servant Enterprises
Harbour View Road,
Broughty Ferry

**Enquiries at the burger van or in person at Stewpot's Bar, Broughty Ferry, after 6pm.
Not Bank Holidays (brings out the nutters).**

Dear BBC Halfwits,

I have just watched the first episode of your documentary on me. Please find enclosed my edit notes. I expect every single one to be acted on with some haste.

1 min: What happened to my theme tune?

3 mins: That is not my body shape. You have used CGI to exaggerate certain areas in order to get a cheap joke. Please show the reality.

5 mins: That is not my running style. I run with a long, elegant gait. You have clearly sped up the footage to give me a more comical, scarpering style. Amend.

6 mins: Actress looked unimpressed when I flirted with her. Do we have another take? Or can you Photoshop in another actress who is capable of giving a more believable reaction?

7 mins: Due to the weakness of the rest of the cast, my joke didn't quite 'land' there. Can you use special effects to make the other actors laugh and shake their heads as if to say, 'Here he goes again'?

8 mins: Eh? Makes no sense.

10 mins: Could you give just the slightest suggestion that I'm aroused in this scene? Just add a telltale 'bump' to the corduroys. Not when I'm holding the cat, though.

12 mins: Too much talking from other actors. Boring!

14 mins: Get the camera on me, please.

16 mins: I'm the shortest actor in this scene, which sends the wrong message. Please shorten the others by a foot each.

19 mins: That is not my smile. Change it.

21 mins: Eh? Makes no sense.

23 mins: You've butchered that joke. Absolutely butchered it.

25 mins: What the hell have you done to my hair? It looks like lady hair. Do you have any idea how that's going to play in Broughty Ferry? You're killing me!

27 mins: That's how I walk now, is it? GET REAL.

29 mins: Oh, here we go. Everyone laughs at Bob, do they? You people are FUCKING IDIOTS.

30 mins: What happened to my theme tune?

Your servant,
Bob Servant

– 4 –

Sad Times Publishing 1

From: Mary Riley
To: Bob Servant
Subject: Can you help?

Dearly Beloved,

My name is Mrs. Mary Riley and I write this to you through my tears of sorrow. I am a dying woman who has decided to donate what I have to charity through you. You may be wondering why I chose you. But someone has to be chosen.

I am 66 years old and have been touched by the lord to donate from what I have inherited from my late husband to charity through you for the good work of humanity. I had good parents who died and now i am careful to stop my husband's bad relatives from to use his hard earned funds inappropriately. I have asked the lord to forgive me all my sins and I believe he has, because He is merciful.

You no idea that problems I have had in my life. It has been so hard from the very start and now I want to give the sum of (GBP 8 Million) to charity through you for the good work of the lord, and to help the motherless, less privileged and also for the assistance of the widows.

At the moment I cannot take any telephone calls, due to the fact that I have been restricted by my doctor from taking telephone calls because I deserve all the rest I can get. Please contact my lawyer with your details though the details attach.

Yours in trust,
Mary Riley

From: Bob Servant
To: Mary Riley
Subject: Quick one

Mary,

Ever thought of writing a book?

Your Servant,
Bob Servant
Managing Editor
Sad Times Publishing

From: Mary Riley
To: Bob Servant
Subject: Re: Quick one

What do you mean by this? Have you contacted my lawyer as the plan?

From: Bob Servant
To: Mary Riley
Subject: Sad Times Publishing

Mary,

Wipe your tears away my friend because I have some news that I think will
lift your chin right up into the clouds. Mary, I am the Managing Editor of a
Scottish publisher called Sad Times Publishing. We're largely looking for
stories like yours, real weepies that will reach into our reader's bodies
through their eyes and play merry hell with their hearts. They're called
misery memoirs over here, Mary, and we've been behind all the big Scottish
ones in recent years such as –

Black, Blue and Hungry Too - The Terrible Story of Jimmy Krankie

Please Dad, Not the Face! - The Awful Life of Andrew Marr

and

*I Just Need(ed) a Friend - How pop band Texas escaped a life of pick-
pocketing to top the Charts.*

Mary, I think your story would fit very comfortably indeed into our collection.
Will you 'lift the biro' for Sad Times Publishing?

Yours,
Bob Servant
Managing Editor
Sad Times Publishing

From: Mary Riley
To: Bob Servant
Subject: Payment

Bob,

Yes I can tell you my terrible story that will be like this others that you have. Please Bob I will tell you my story and now can maybe an advance payment to be helpful my dear? I took it upon myself as a challenge to God that i must fulfill a charity deed in life. There are more you don't know about me and If you agree with me to have my full story you will have to do what i have requested. What is the pay? It will boost my charity giving. Whenever I think about my life I cry and I cry now just thinking about what I have been through.

Mary

From: Bob Servant
To: Mary Riley
Subject: Dry those old eyes

Mary,

Stop crying for God's sake, you'll get me started and when I cry I don't mess about. In 1982 I cried for four days after watching ET. For the first two days I was crying because I thought it was a documentary and for the next two days I was crying because someone told me that it wasn't.

Mary, I'm interested in your story and don't you worry about the money side of things. If you want to get rich then write yourself a book that does 'not bad' in Scotland and from then on everything you touch turns, sometimes literally, to gravy. I've done a few books myself and I attach a photo of my house. For now can you just give me the best stuff from your story. What's the very worst thing that's happened to you?

All the best,
Bob Servant
Managing Editor
Sad Times Publishing

16

---

16 This isn't Bob's house. In fact, it's the Monifieth home of Snow Patrol keyboardist Tom 'Tommy' Simpson. This photo copyright © Scottish Celebrity Homes Magazine Ltd.

From: Mary Riley
To: Bob Servant
Subject: This for now

Dear beloved Bob

i am so happy that you want to use my story to write a book that will touch peoples lives. Well I will give you just some for now but you must know because of the money $8m (million) that I have I have been in danger for some time. In fact several attempts to assassinate me have been made but all their plans keeps failing them. I cannot believe really I would have not been dead by now. You see Bob this is a story you will not believe and it will be a success for you. Now let us talk of a payment and we can enter the next level of my story. If this is your house like you say a first payment wil be easy for you

Mary Riley

From: Bob Servant
To: Mary Riley
Subject: I like it Mary, I like it a lot

Mary,

This is all great stuff. People love a good assassination story. Just look at JFK or when Sir Trevor McDonald shot his postman.[17] Can you give me a bit more of what we call 'colour' on the assassination attempt? I presume he had a gun?

Also for the title of your book I've had a wee think and I'm considering the options below.

Every Cloud Has a Lining of More Cloud - My Hell by Mary Riley

Don't Shoot! - The Mary Riley Story

Jesus Christ, He's Got A Gun! - The Life and Times of Mary Riley

I'll have a go at the 'blurb' for the cover now as well,

Cheers,
Bob

---

[17] The former television newsreader Sir Trevor McDonald has never shot a postman. He did, however, strangle his milkman in 1978. See *Your Headlines Tonight: The Trevor McDonald Story* p. 104 ('I waited behind the dustbins until I saw him make his way up the path then sprung out like a panther and wrapped my hands around his neck. Afterwards I felt sick. I called Nicholas Witchell who told his wife he was opening a new Presto supermarket in Titchfield and drove straight round in his Volvo estate. We buried the milkman in a shallow grave on the edge of the New Forest. I remember Nicholas lightening the mood while we struggled to lift the milkman's body by joking that the milkman was "full fat". I always appreciated Nicholas for making that joke at what was a difficult time for me, and I would like to thank him again in print. Thank you, Nicholas, and, as the saying goes, I still owe you a pint! And not of milk!')

From: Mary Riley
To: Bob Servant
Subject: This for now

Well Bob I was shot at by a bandit who wanted my money and the bullet hit in the shoulder and I was in hospital for months before well enough to continue with the charity. After the attack i resolved with the plan of my late husbands attorney to wear a bullet proof vest always. It is OK whatever you want to call the book and I believe this is enough and will give you more stories when i get to hear your offer. I must go now because I am weak now do not forget how sick i am bob and your payment for my story will go all on medicine.

Mary Riley

From: Bob Servant
To: Mary Riley
Subject: What do you think?

Mary,

OK that's good news that you were shot. It will make the book reach out from the shelves and grab the reader by the balls. Right, Mary, I've been busy at this end. Have a look at the attached, it's the cover and the opening page of the book which I think lets us really hit the ground running. Let me know what you reckon, I've added a couple of little tweaks but it's largely based on what you've told me.

Hope you like it!

Bob Servant
Managing Editor
Sad Times Publish

Mary Riley has seen so much life she should be five hundred years old. Raised by wolves in the mountains, Riley grew up communicating only in whistles. At the tender age of 43, she was rescued by Buffalo Bill who told her to go back to school. After becoming "head girl" Mary was walking along the road one day when she was kidnapped by the rebels and slung into a prison on an island. After escaping from the island by pretending to be a penguin Mary was walking along the road (a different road to before) one day when a bandit jumped out of a cave and started taking potshots at her. One bullet hit her shoulder and the other scraped her lovely head. Now, in BOTH BARRELS, Mary Riley tells her story for the first time. You'll be shocked and confused and happy and sad and excited. You'll shake your head and say "come on" but honestly this stuff is straight up and is coming out of the horse's mouth. Can YOU handle BOTH BARRELS?

Both Barrels
The Life and Times of Mary Riley

Chapter One

Bang Bang!

More than anything, I remember his eyes. They were like big pieces of coal.

'Are you Mary Riley?' asked the bandit.

I had never told a lie in my life. I was brought up by some of the most honest wolves you could ever meet.

'Yes,' I told him. His eyes were like big saucers of oil.

'You die Mary Riley,' he said. His voice was like a drum being played by an elephant.

He fired the gun. It sounded like all the babies in the world crying and this is a metaphor because it was the moment I lost my innocence.

The bullet hit my shoulder.

'Ah you fucking bastard!' I shouted. 'You shot me in the fucking shoulder you fucking prick what is fucking wrong with you, you total fucking nob jockey!'

'You die Mary Riley,' he said again. His eyes were like pigeons.

Everything went black. When I awoke it was just me and the wolves.

'Oh dear Mary,' said the main wolf. 'Oh dear, oh dear, oh dear.'

From: Mary Riley
To: Bob Servant
Subject: Time for payment

Bob it is exciting to see the book all together but this is not how i would speak with the bad language. I told you i am a charity giver and lover of God so why would i speak like this please change it. other things wrong also with the wolves and the prison because i have never committed a crime bob can't you see the crime has all been done on me. and why would the wolves be there because i told you i had good parents.

Ok bob you have had a lot from me and this book will now be a big success for you and your house will grow bigger even so send me now $5000 bob you know this is fair here is western union information send today bob.

NAME: MARY RILEY
COUNTRY: NIGERIA
STATE: LAGOS
BRANCH: CENTRE
TEST QUESTION: MARY
TEST ANSWER: RILEY

From: Bob Servant
To: Mary Riley
Subject: Could you handle Rice?

Mary,

Thanks for the feedback. Unfortunately the bad language has to stay. I don't like it myself but because of computer games and rappers such as Biggie Smalls and Nick Berry all the kids are used to famous people speaking like dockers and, sadly, that includes you. It would actually work in our favour if you could develop what the nippers call a 'beef' with someone else in the public eye. Would you mind if I send out a press release where you challenge Aneka Rice to a fight? Photo attached, think you could you take her?

Yours,
Bob Servant

Managing Editor
Sad Times Publishing

From: Mary Riley
To: Bob Servant
Subject: How can i fight when i am dying

What is this what are you talking about. I will not fight someone and i only doing the book because you have asked me. where is my payment? I am not taking part in this any more until you make me payment immediately of $1000. that is more than fair.

From: Bob Servant
To: Mary Riley
Subject: Rice

Mary,

Things have backfired a bit. Aneka Rice wants your home address, can you send it over? She is actually very fit for her age and I can't help thinking it was a bit daft of you to publicly challenge her to a fight in your condition. Under these circumstances I'm afraid we can no longer represent you here at Sad Times. While we don't mind signing up people with a bit of an edge, you seem to be dangerously unhinged Mary and I think it would be best for everyone if we go our separate ways.

Yours in fear,
Bob Servant
Managing Editor
Sad Times Publishing

NO REPLY

Dear Bob,

How did you first get into the burger business? I can only imagine the excitement of those early days for you and Frank.

Alan Forsyth, Nottingham

* * * * *

Alan,

My time in the (sometimes literally) Dog-Eat-Dog, Dundee Cheeseburger Scene was very much the Golden Age of both my life and career. It all began in the summer of 1981, when I stood in a Dundee scrapyard and looked at a van that had seen better days. But there was something about it, a certain "Johnny Say Qwa". "She'll do" I whispered. "She'll do". Unfortunately, two days later the brakes went on the Kingsway, I nearly wiped out a van full of what were either Cub Scouts or tiny soldiers, and I had to urgently set fire to the van for legal reasons.

But once I got a better van, and appointed Frank as my Acting Deputy Director of Sauces, my career went from strength to strength. Forty years ago, I was the fifth most successful cheeseburger van owner in the wider Dundee area. After four decades of hard work, innovation, positive mental attitude, spatula practice and two deaths, I am up to third.

Along the way I invented the concept of the novelty burger, starting with my Belgrano Burger in '82, along with my trademarked Onion Fountain, and bravely rode out the horrors of Dundee's infamous Cheeseburger Wars of the 1980s[18] .

They were great days, Alan. For all of us. Apart from the folk who died.

Bob

~~~~~~~~~~~

---

[18] The Dundee Courier, 20th May 1987, "The Day The Spatulas Cried"...

Bob,

You are, clearly, a very famous man. How do you manage the demands of your adoring public?

Carol Hilsum, Epsom

* * * * *

Carol,

It ain't (isn't) easy. Having the third busiest cheeseburger van in Dundee projected me into the stratosphere. It was as if space boffins had fitted a rocket to the business end of my body and sent me on an intergalactic journey to a planet called Fame. But being famous can be a tough shift. The Scottish tradition of 'Build 'em up, knock 'em down' is something me and my famous pals have a rueful laugh about. I'm close to most of the Scottish big guns. Sean Connery and I were firm friends ever since we met at a jumble sale in St Andrews in 1983. I made a joke about a pair of china dogs, a well-worked piece of observational comedy about whether or not they produced china excrement, which had Sean weeping with laughter, and we stayed largely in touch ever since.

The Krankies and I had a weekend in Dunfermline in the early nineties that was, to cut a long story short, like the Last Days of Rome, and I was fortunate enough to meet Sir Alex Ferguson in the car park of a Little Chef just outside Carlisle in 2003. I had been in England on a wild goose chase concerning an industrial lettuce slicer, and Sir Alex had been, his words, 'going somewhere'. We had a good laugh about the fact he, his words, 'really had to go' and I did some old school physical comedy by standing in front of his car and doing a funny 'don't shoot' gesture, which brought out some of Alex's trademark comedy, as he launched into a tongue-in-cheek barrage of abuse at me which ended with him accidentally calling me a "a prick" while accidentally running over my foot.

Some vanners handle the limelight better than others. Stage fright is the great enemy. I have seen truly great vanners, wake up one day and find themselves unable to open the hatch. Not me. No matter how blue I might feel, I open the hatch and let the punter love wash over me like hot lava. On a good day, it is as if I open the hatch, and the entire population of Broughty Ferry are waiting to unleash upon me what I can only describe as a tsunami of love that cascades down all over my face and body while I squeeze my eyes closed and shout "I love it, I love it, I absolutely love it".

In short, it's fine,

Bob

Hi Bob,

I'm trying to get promoted at work, but how do I go about it? Have you ever officially promoted Frank on the van? I'm a lawyer but I'm pretty sure the same rules apply,

Mark Young, London

* * * * *

Mark,

Frank has had a meteoric rise on the van. Like any apprentice he started on the napkins, but after just nine years, was handed a shock promotion to Deputy Manager (Onions). Just 12 years later, he was handed his dream job, Director of Sauces, the so-called 'floating role' of the cheeseburger-van trade. Fast-forward to today and Frank is nearing the end of his apprenticeship and will enter a five-year appraisal to see if he is ready to earn bumper, 'full-time' wage. Yes, he's been lucky but he's worked for it and he deserves the riches that might one day arrive. I trust his story will prove an inspiration to you.

Yours in hope,
Bob

Bob,

In tribute to your good self I'm thinking of starting a burger van. Would you consider sharing your 'recipe for success'?

Jimmy Walker, Leeds

* * * * *

I enclose my award-winning guide. Please send £5.99 by return of post.

"Minced Meat
Making Burgers th

Meat

If you're serious about running a burger van then you need a lot of meat. We buy a heavy bin-bag of meat every morning from a fun-loving butcher in Carnoustie. We use a 'collage' of meat, which is pretty much as good as it gets.

Buns

'Come and have some fun in a bun!' is our famous battle cry and it brings the punters sprinting from their little punter houses with their mouths hanging open like lizards. The great thing about serving buns is the vast opportunities for double, if not triple, entendres. It's no coincidence that our van attracts an alarming number of divorcees, eager for some near-the-knuckle bawdy fun (in a bun).

and Dreams"
Bob Servant Way

Lettuce

Introduced by the eighties 'Yuppie' movement as part of their 'loadsamoney' culture was the idea of having bits of lettuce with cheeseburgers. In 1987 I invented the One-Finger Lettuce Shredder (™). I have, almost literally, never looked back.

Onions

We serve 'triple-cooked' onions extremely hot as an onion 'lava'.

Sauces

Frank is Director of Sauces. Not my problem.

Napkins

Two for adults and one for kids. Otherwise I will – and please believe me on this – make you wish that you'd never been born.

Dear Bob,

I am in a six-piece combo band in the Glasgow area and we're looking to take the next step up. We've just finished a two-week residency that saw us sell out both the lounge and bar area of Cathcart Bowling Club. We've gone as far as we can go in Glasgow, and want to crack the lucrative East Coast market. We're talking, of course, about Broughty Ferry. Would you be interest in managing us, Bob? I've heard you're the Colonel Tom of the East Coast, the Brian Epstein of the Ferry. Please help.

Yours faithfully,

Richard (top drawer drummer), Belle and Sebastian

* * * * *

Richard,

Yes, I am available to be your Svengali, but with some fairly straightforward conditions: -

1. Most of the time, I will reward you with individual arms round the shoulders and gentle encouragement. However, when I think it is necessary, I will also give each of you an absolute rocket. They will be uncomfortable situations for us both but will be to the long-term benefit of the band, and that's my only concern.
2. Album covers will be dominated by photos of me doing the splits in leather trousers (using CGI) (for the splits, not the trousers)
3. The tour bus. Downstairs will be kitchen, bathroom and some 'bucket seats' for the band. Upstairs will be Bob's No-Rules Party Zone (NRPZ) for rock 'n' (and) roll madness – telling rude limericks, giving each other love bites, eating jelly with our hands, etc.
4. Every song on the albums will end with me saying, 'And that's that!'

Bob

* * * * *

Bob,

Deal.

Richard

Dear Bob,

I'm looking for some advice on my upcoming wedding. As an actor people are expecting a first-class groom's speech but, as I usually have my lines written for me, I'm a tad nervous. I was hoping a renowned public speaker like yourself could give me some tips on winning over a crowd?

Much appreciated,

Martin Compston, Greenock

* * * * *

Martin,

A lot of people get the groom speech all wrong. They think they have to bang on about the bride, how she's one of the good guys and a safe pair of hands and so on, but that only serves to make the groom look desperately weak. The groom's speech is a chance to show the bride's family that you are a strong man, willing to make brave choices and stand up for yourself. The best way to do that is to open your speech with a sustained attack of bawdy jokes on an elderly relative on your wife's side. A 'shock and awe' onslaught against this kindly individual will show the guests that you are your own man. They'll hand you an ovation that you will never forget while your wife simpers with delight at your daring.

Yours in hope,
Bob

Bob,

What would be your dream cheeseburger-dinner-party line-up, living or, God forbid, dead?

Rufus Jones, Brighton

* * * * *

Rufus,
Souness, Navratilova, Mallett.
Yours in hope,
Bob

– 5 –

The Vanishing Beard

From: Alistair Ross
To: Bob Servant
Subject: Do Not Ignore This

Dear Respected Sir,

I got your contact email address through internet research as i was conducting researches to link-up a reliable foreign partner to help me carry out this transaction. On coming accross your contact, i was touched spiritually and physically to connect you, with great feelings that you might be of great help to me.

I live here in Australia and work for the Australia Investments Corp. To be very honest with you, this business i have introduced to you is very genuine and highly benefitial. i have the absolute convinction that you will neither betray nor disappoint me in this transaction. I have access to a fund which if is not claimed after eight years it will enter into the bank's treasury and becomes the inherittance of the Australian government but instead I could transfer to you.

If this sounds like what you want and need then contacts me right away. Please trust in me just as i have trusted you before opening the secret of this business to you because about 99.9% of all genuine transactions all over the world is based on mutual trust and understanding. You will see the form to fill in here.

Thanks and best regards
Alistair Ross
Australia Investments Corp

From: Bob Servant
To: Alistair Ross
Subject: Quick snap?

Hi Alistair,

Sounds great, can you please send a photo of yourself for my records?
Your Servant,

Bob Servant

From: Alistair Ross
To: Bob Servant
Subject: This is no problem

Hello bob yes this is no problem for photo here is me in my private office. Ok well now we can procede?

From: Bob Servant
To: Alistair Ross
Subject: Let's lose the beard

Morning champ,

OK here is my position. I don't like beards, Alistair, I don't like them at all. About forty years ago I saw a documentary about a guy with a beard who led a gang of young pickpockets in London and then one of the kids started singing as if someone had his little balls in a vice and the whole thing was awful.[19]

The situation is almost laughably simple. Simply shave off your beard and sit back in that same chair in that same office and send me a new photo. I will then send you every single penny I have as well as my neighbour Frank's pension book.

Don't get me wrong, Alistair, I can see your potential. You are wearing a sandwich board saying 'Opportunity', a top hat saying 'Trust Me' and, if I may, a pair of pants embroidered with the phrase 'Work Hard' at the front and, if I may, 'Play Hard', at the back.

    That last bit was largely metaphors.
    Look forward to seeing the new photo,

Bob

---

[19] I think, and indeed hope, that Bob is referring to the 1968 film adaptation of Oliver Twist.

From: Alistair Ross
To: Bob Servant
Subject: I cannot do this

Bob,

I cannot do this because my wife likes my beard and in fact it was her idea. If you're married man then this will work for you. Just fill in the form or if you want to send your whole money for investment purposes this is fine too. Thank you for the metaphor i get message and you right this is 'OPPORTUNITY' and i will so hard for you you will be amazed.

Alistair

From: Bob Servant
To: Alistair Ross
Subject: Stand up to her

Alistair,

Don't let your wife be your boss. You'll end up like Richard Madeley who famously has to ask Judy before he goes to the toilet.[20] If you want to do business then the beard has to go.

Bob

From: Alistair Ross
To: Bob Servant
Subject: Not important

Bob,

The beard does not matter in business bob you must know this. Send your information anyway.

Alistair

From: Bob Servant
To: Alistair Ross
Subject: Goodbye

Alistair,

I have made my position clear.

Goodbye,

Bob

---

[20] I have failed to find any concrete evidence that the television presenter Richard Madeley (67) asks his wife for permission to go to the toilet, but that doesn't mean it's not true.

From: Alistair Ross
To: Bob Servant
Subject: Forget the beard

Bob

Come on this is not important and why does photo have to be the same. You don't trust me! bob why not? Send the information.

Alistair

From: Alistair Ross
To: Bob Servant
Subject: Answer me

Bob?

not heard from you, send something today.

From: Alistair Ross
To: Bob Servant
Subject: OK here it is

OK Bob here is photo like you ask, I have removed my beard even if it causes problem with my wife. Now send your data now or if you want whole money invested I have many opportunities that you will like.

From: Bob Servant
To: Alistair Ross
Subject: RE: OK here it is

Please tell me that you're joking.

From: Alistair Ross
To: Bob Servant
Subject: Of course not a joke

Bob this is business not joking what is problem?

From: Bob Servant
To: Alistair Ross
Subject: Have a guess

What do you think the problem might be?

From: Alistair Ross
To: Bob Servant
Subject: RE: Have a guess

i really do not know bob can you send me your details to arrange investment?

From: Bob Servant
To: Alistair Ross
Subject: Come on Alistair

Alistair,

If you said you were joking, I would have all the respect in the world for you.

Bob

From: Alistair Ross
To: Bob Servant
Subject: OK

ok i am joking does that help?

From: Bob Servant
To: Alistair Ross
Subject: Love

Alistair,

I may, I repeat may, have fallen in love with you,

Bob

Hi Bob,

Our son has his first date at the weekend, the poor wee lad's a nervous wreck. We were hoping a man of your vast experience could advise us on how to support him at this challenging time?

Shuggy and Sara P, Inverness

* * * * *

Great question,

You can support him by letting him have a wee 'run through'. Set up your kitchen as a fancy restaurant and invite your son in. For that all-important element of surprise it would be best if you, Shuggy, played the girl. Dress extremely provocatively and make various daring suggestions involving the black pepper. Sara, you will, inevitably, be playing the part of a lewd Italian waiter. Teach your son about the danger of male competition by flirting outrageously with Shuggy, having padded out your trousers to suggest your waiter character is in an excitable state. Your son will be put through a baptism of fire and will thank you for it, both now and in later years when he is happily married to a woman who may or may not resemble his father in drag.

All the best,
Bob

Dear Bob,

How do you like to relax?

John Gordon Sinclair

* * * * *

Dear JGS,

I relax in the same way most men of my position do so. By writing high-end romantic fiction,

Yours,
Bob

FIFTY SHADES OF BROUGHTY FERRY – BOB SERVANT

Chapter One
"An Extension Full of Sauce"

We shouldn't have been doing this. It was extremely naughty. She was married. And I was supposed to be at the bowling: a play-off with Fintry, for the chance to go up to the Super League. 'Ooh,' she said. 'Nice place you have here.' 'Yes,' I replied. 'It's an extension. Though you wouldn't know it, the way it blends in.'

I'd met the woman earlier that day in Safeway. I had made a lengthy but layered joke in the vegetable aisle and she had laughed like a docker. She complimented me on the way I was handling a courgette. 'Ooh,' she said. 'Are you good at handling anything else?' 'Cucumbers,' I replied. 'Or the odd parsnip.' After a bit more back and forth about bananas, I became aware that the woman was not really talking about bananas but was, in fact, being highly suggestive. I'm good at picking up signals and I'm all too aware of my effect on women, particularly in Safeway. And particularly in the vegetable section.

So now here we are, back in the extension, saucing things up like we've just got out of prison. 'You're very dirty,' I say to the woman. 'Ooh,' she replies, 'Yes, I am.' 'You really are,' I say, pointing to the mud on her dungarees. 'I've been working on the berries,' she says. 'How much do you get per punnet these days?' I ask. '15p,' she replies. 'Would you like to see my strawberries?' 'Not really,' I say. 'I like blackberries. I'm a blackberry nut.' 'I'd like to see your blackberries,' she says. 'They're not in season,' I reply.

'I'll be the judge of that,' she says, smiling like a murderer. 'I apologise profusely if I've got this wrong,' I say, 'but are you referring to my testicles?' 'Yes, I am,' she says, 'I bet they're absolutely mouth-watering.' 'They're just normal testicles,' I tell her. 'Like you see on the TV.'

'Listen,' she says, pointing again to the mud on her dungarees. 'Maybe you'd like to punish me, for being so dirty?' 'Fair enough,' I reply. 'How about a small fine. Call it a fiver?' 'Is there any other way I could pay?' she asks, with a strange smile. 'Well,' I reply, 'I suppose I could take a cheque. Though it seems daft, for such a small amount.' 'Let's get this party started!' she says, and, right there in the extension, she whips off her jumper. I look in wonder at what lies beneath. It's another jumper. 'That one will be coming off too,' she says. 'In a bit.'

– 6 –

The Sea Could Not Take Him, No Woman Could Tame Him

From: Colin Jackson
To: Bob Servant
Subject: Job Offer

Good Day,

My name is Mr Colin Jackson an artist in the United Kingdom. I have been selling my art works for the last 3 years to galleries and private collectors all around the world but am always facing serious difficulties as people are always offering to pay with financial instruments that I am not familiar with.

I undergo so much difficulty in converting them to cash and am currently in search of a representative who I am willing to pay 15% each transaction. You would receive payments, convert them to cash, deduct 15% and send the remaining funds to me. If you have read and understood my offer, please indicate your willingness to work for me.

Best Regards
Colin Jackson

From: Bob Servant
To: Colin Jackson
Subject: I would love to see your work?

Colin,

Thank you for getting in touch and for thinking of me for this unique proposal. Well done on sticking with your art. So many creative folk give up at the first hurdle and it is really heartening that you have swum against the tide. Could you possibly email me some examples of your work? I am currently looking to redecorate and maybe they could be just the ticket,

Your Servant,
Bob Servant

From: Colin Jackson
To: Bob Servant
Subject: Here you go Bob

Hello Bob,

Thanks for getting back to me, i really appreciate you taking your time to reply to my job offer and also being interested in working with me as a business partner. I have attached a picture of my artwork as you asked, hope you will love it and it becomes my ticket lol!

Actually why i need you is as a cashier where you take out your percentage as agreed from every payment. Since you the first person to respond to my offer then I will consider you as my first choice of cashier which am going to give a trial? The information i will require from you will be

Your Full Name

Full Address

Contact Phone

Next we will talk about banking details. Hope everything is being understood here, waiting to hear from you.

Colin Jackson

From: Bob Servant
To: Colin Jackson
Subject: You have an exceptional talent

Colin,

Thank you so much for sending that example, which is a stunning piece. I've always been a plum fan and, I must say, I had a hunch that you would be too.

I would love to buy some of your art Colin. Do you have any paintings of ships? I live right beside the river Tay and I often sit in the garden, especially in the summer, drinking room temperature Midori out of a well-handled mug, watching the boats, wearing a pair of deliberately snug corduroy shorts. And they said I'd never make it!

I think it would be great to have a few boats on the walls in the house. There's another reason as well for me wanting a boat painting, to be honest, but I'm a little embarrassed to say.

Bob

From: Colin Jackson
To: Bob Servant
Subject: Thank You

Thanks Bob,

It's a pleasure hearing from you, I am truly flattered. I have not many paintings of ships but I do have one that is below.[21] Do you like it? Let me know what you think and also if you are still going to work with me as a cashier or a customer? It is a cashier I need but I will not turn down a customer! lol sounds funny Bob.

Thanks again for your mail looking for your reply.

Colin

From: Bob Servant
To: Colin Jackson
Subject: A Proposition

Colin,

That is absolutely enchanting. It is so life-like Colin, I feel like stripping naked and diving through my computer screen into the water.

I would prefer a slightly different painting. As I touched on before, there is something else I should tell you. You see, Colin, I used to be in the Merchant Navy. It was during my wilderness years before I hit the glory days of the cheeseburger vans. That much is true but in actual fact I never set foot on a boat after a genuine misunderstanding during a training exercise.

In the, sometimes literally, "dog eat dog" pubs of Broughty Ferry I have occasionally exaggerated my Merchant Navy career. I've told them all sorts - that I captained my own ship called 'Bob's Beauty', that I had a wife on a tropical island who could juggle coconuts using only self-belief and the left hand side of her bottom and that I once knocked out a shark with an opportunistic head butt.

What I would love is a painting where there is a man in quite a big boat but you can't see his face? Then I could say that it is a painting of me in 'Bob's Beauty' from the late 1970s. Maybe you could paint some flares on the man or suggest he's just made a risqué joke that these days would have him instantly removed from the set of a daytime television show. What do you think? I have a fair bit of money stashed away for situations like this, which arise a lot more than you'd expect.

Bob Servant

---

[21] At this point Mr Jackson provided a wonderful photo of a harbour scene but the image was badly corrupted. When I informed Bob of this he responded that he had some photos at home that were 'a lot more corrupt than that'. This was an observation that Bob found so amusing I momentarily thought he might choke to death on his sandwich.

From: Colin Jackson
To: Bob Servant
Subject: I could do this

Ok Bob,

Really a funny story bob, what you are asking for is not impossible i can do it for you, with your name printed on it like you said 'Bob's Beauty' but its going to cost you quite a lot of money for such a thing. It is not a problem for me but you have to pay part of the money in advance to assure me that you will pick it up so my effort won't be wasted. so if you wish then send me the following –

Your picture that you will like to see on the painting The color combination that you wish

The advance of $1000 then the balance of $1500 when your painting gets to you

I will be updating you on how the work progresses. The money should be sent through Western Union. I will be waiting for your mail,

Colin

From: Bob Servant
To: Colin Jackson
Subject: Anything kicking about your studio?

Colin,

Great to hear from you. I'd love to get this painting on the go but I worry that if you paint the thing from scratch then it will take ages. I'm having a 'Pernod and Push-ups Party' in a fortnight and I'd really like the painting for that. Do you have a painting of a man on a boat that we can just pretend is me? Maybe it's in the distance so people would not know? If so, then I could just buy that,

Bob

From: Colin Jackson
To: Bob Servant
Subject: I have one

Hello Bob,

Really do not have the exact painting you are looking for but something close to that, picture below. Let me know what you think. I am happy to sell it but it is a little expensive.[22]

Thanks

---

[22] Here Mr Jackson kindly sent a photo of a contented-looking gentleman looking out with binoculars at a sunset from a ship's bridge. An action, I should say, that I have always been led to believe could lead to instant blindness. Anyway, the photo contains certain identifiable aspects aspects of where he nicked it from.

From: Bob Servant
To: Colin Jackson
Subject: Bob Looking out to sea

Colin,

That is perfect. I think we could call it 'Bob Looking Out To Sea' and say it shows me looking out from the bridge of Bob's Beauty, looking for icebergs perhaps? What do you think? Does that sound believable to you?

One thing I noticed was that, in the silhouette of my image I am wearing a floppy hat. I don't think that this is what a captain would wear and attach a photo of a more appropriate hat for the final image.

Your friend,
Bob

From: Colin Jackson
To: Bob Servant
Subject: You must decide

Hey Bob,

It will be a lot of work for me to edit the hat on the already made painting with the one you have sent me, is almost a new job so Bob but I will do but is this really the hat of a ship captain? Let me know so we can save time instead of this stress. If you wanted a new painting it would have been almost ready by now! So make up your mind and let me know.

Thanks
Colin

From: Bob Servant
To: Colin Jackson
Subject: Painting

Colin,

Maybe I should go for the existing painting. I could tell people that the reason I was wearing the floppy hat was because it was taken during my break? What do you think? Would you believe that? And, more importantly, would you believe that if you were a woman Colin?

I am desperate to fix something up on the skirt front because Tommy Peanuts recently got together with Daphne Silverstone, the barmaid at Stewpot's Bar. Daphne, I must admit, is a real diamond. She's not as young as she was but my God she still has them hanging over the bar down at Stewpot's. I'm sometimes one of the hangers myself! And why not?!

She has all sorts of moves. Whenever someone orders an apple juice she'll give it – 'Oooh, I feel quite fruity myself', and do that thing where you pretend your eyeballs are rolling backwards into your head. Or if a punter asks if they do sandwiches she'll say, 'Ooooh, are you asking if you can nibble on my buns?' and do the old double-point at her bits and bobs while everyone cheers and bangs their glasses on the bar.

It's all basic, knockabout stuff but with Daphne it just doesn't seem tacky. Anyway, Tommy has somehow squired himself up with Daphne and is walking about the Ferry like he's John Wayne and he keeps pretending to have a bad back just so he can wink and make some rude comment about how he got it.

So the pressure's on to come up with something. And this painting could be my way in.

Bob

From: Colin Jackson
To: Bob Servant
Subject: Yes I would believe this for sure

Hey Bob,

I think that's exactly what you should tell them, that the picture was taken during a break. Anybody will believe that. Women as well, and this painting will be a big help on you find your own Daphne. Are we now agreed? I can do a special deal but you will have to pay in advance.

Colin

From: Bob Servant
To: Colin Jackson
Subject: YES YOU'RE RIGHT COLIN

Hi Colin,

You're right, there's no reason why the figure in the painting shouldn't be me. Even captains have to take breaks sometimes. Also, I was thinking I could buy a hat like the one in the painting and start wearing it about the place.

Colin, I would love to see a photo of you at work on a painting or in a studio, is this possible? I'm not being nosey! I just love artists and it would be fantastic to see you at work?

Many thanks,
Captain Bob

From: Colin Jackson
To: Bob Servant
Subject: Myself in studio

Hello Bob,

How are you doing? I am OK just been a little busy with work. You should know i am a busy man . . . lol. My pictures at work attached below,[23] then i would really like to make a fresh painting of you in Bob's Beauty? You must finally make up your mind once and for all and tell me what you think i am not always able to check my mail. Looking for your mail. ASAP.

Thanks
Colin

From: Bob Servant
To: Colin Jackson
Subject: Painting Final Order!

Colin,

Great to hear from you and thank you so much for those pictures. I love seeing you working, you look as if you are totally lost in the moment, adrift in the world of art. I have decided! I want a large painting of the image you have shown me, with 'Captain Bob' (wink wink!) looking out to sea. I would like it framed in a gold frame, or one that looks gold (wink wink!) and underneath I would like the inscription – **'Captain Bob Servant bravely looks out from the bridge of Bob's Beauty. Valentines Day, 1978, somewhere in the Indian Ocean.'**

---

[23] At this point Mr Jackson supplied several photos of an artist working in a studio. The images have been removed for legal reasons. The images have been removed for legal reasons, as they are highly unlikely to feature Mr Jackson.

And then, underneath that, the quotation:

'The Sea Could Not Take Him, No Woman Could Tame Him, No Mountain Too Tall, No River Too Deep, Deep Like His Heart. Bob Servant, Simply The Best. Rocking All Over The World. Be Lucky'.

Sound OK? I would like the painting to be done in a "gloss finish" and to measure 2m long and around 1.5m high as that would look magic above my second sofa. I am very excited by this Colin, very excited indeed.

Bob

PS Bit of a debate with Chappy Williams at the Eagle Inn last night Colin. As an artist, do you think in words or pictures? I said I thought you would think in pictures but Chappy said that was a load of shite?

From: Colin Jackson
To: Bob Servant
Subject: OK

Hello Bob,

About your painting i will do the art work and all the words you want me to print on it sounds OK because it makes you look like a brave captain or rather a hero, lol.

I looking forward to get your mail ASAP and it very important that you send your advance through Western Union so I can get started on Bob's Beauty! Then the job will be ready within 12 days.

Yes Bob we do think in pictures, I have spent more than 90% of my adulthood in studios painting and thinking of what my customers will appreciate making it as real as possible. When I go shopping with my wife i often stare at things that are around me, imagining them in pictures and dreaming of making paintings of everything I see.

Well hope u are having a nice day. Let me know when you have sent the money Bob.

Colin

From: Bob Servant
To: Colin Jackson
Subject: YOU'RE GOING TO BE IN THE PAPER!

Colin,

I have interesting news! First of all, I have the money ordered and will have it tomorrow. The second is that I was just in the Royal Arch looking for skirt and bumped into Chappy Williams again. He has just landed the big one - Broughty Ferry correspondent for the Evening Telegraph. I spoke to him about the fact you were doing this painting for me and he was very, very excited. He wants to interview you for the paper! I told him that you are a busy man so he is only going to send you a few questions. I will send you the article when it comes out.

Please REMEMBER, two things –

He thinks I was a real captain of Bob's Beauty! Make sure you say that.

Please say that I am very handsome if he asks. That will help me with the skirt and Christ knows I need all the help I can get.

Thank you my friend,
Bob

From: Colin Jackson
To: Bob Servant
Subject: Interview

Hello Captain Bob,

Thanks for your mail and interest in me, but I want to know will the interview be through mail or something? Secondly I will do just like you said {captain in the Bob's Beauty} so you have nothing to worry about because we are in this together. Then about the money how did you send it? You should send it through Western Union or Moneygram as it will be available for pick-up instantly. You need to send it now, it is very important as we must get this thing started. Let me know when you have done this and Bob's Beauty will kick off.

Have a wonderful day.
Colin

From: Chappy Williams
To: Colin Jackson
Subject: Interview

HELLO COLIN, I AM CHAPPY, A FRIEND OF BOB SERVANT AND A TOP DRAWER NEWSPAPER REPORTER. I HAVE SOME QUESTIONS FOR YOU FOR AN EXCLUSIVE INTERVIEW. PLEASE SEND ME THE ANSWERS AS SOON AS YOU CAN. THANK YOU, CHAPPY.

How long have you been an artist and what was it that made you start?
Bob said that you think in pictures, can you please explain?
How did you meet Bob?

You are doing a painting of Bob in a boat, is it true that he was a captain in the merchant navy? (I have my doubts)

Do you think he is handsome?
What is your favourite thing about Bob?
If you weren't a painter then what do you think you would be?
As a painter, who is your favourite cartoon character? (Mickey Mouse etc)

Thank you very much,
Chappy Williams, Broughty Ferry Correspondent

From: Colin Jackson
To: Bob Servant
Subject: Chappy

Hello Bob,

Your friend Chappy has sent me the questions for the newspaper. Do you want me to answer them in a way that will suit you?

Colin

From: Bob Servant
To: Colin Jackson
Subject: Re: Chappy

Hello Colin,
100% Yes.

Bob

From: Colin Jackson
To: Chappy Williams
Subject: ANSWERS

Thanks Chappy if you need more information on me you know how to get to me. Tell Bob that I am very grateful for this interview and I am looking forward to read the paper.

Thanks and have a nice day.
Colin

How long have you been an artist and what was it that made you start?
My father was an artists so it has always been part of me but I can say that when I officially opened up to the world as a painter was in 1995 when I inherited his studio and became officially know as painter Colin...lol. So I will say that I have been a painter for about 12 years now.

Bob said that you think in pictures can you please explain this?
Well as a painter I actually think in pictures because everything I see around me I imagine them in painting and how they will look if they painted in pictures, so I really imagine a lot of things in paintings especially when I am at work in my studio. I think in pictures as Bob says.

How did you meet Bob?
Well I met Bob on the internet while I was looking for a representative. Bob got my mail and replied asking to see some of my paintings. He grow interest in me and since then I and Bob have been good friends because he is fun talking to and also a caring fellow to know.

You are doing a painting of Bob in a boat, is it true that he was a captain in the Merchant Navy?
Yes I am doing a painting of Bob in Bob's Beauty. For as long as I have been talking to him I know him as Captain Bob because from the day I met him he

told me he was a captain in the merchant navy and I believe he is a captain, so if I am asked if Bob is a captain I will say yes.

Do you think he is handsome?
Yes Bob must have been handsome when he was younger because he has worked hard in his jobs to earn a lot of money and so would have got fit along the way. With his good jokes also you can imagine how good he would been with women? I just think the skirts would have been on cue for Bob at his young days! Yes he is a handsome man!

What is your favourite thing about Bob?
My favourite thing about Bob is that he sounds like a good man and I am always pleased to read his mails because he is usually interesting in his writing. Bob must be fun being around.

If you weren't a painter then what do you think you would be?
I would have loved to be an international journalist.

As a painter, who is your favourite cartoon character?
My favourite cartoon is Tom and Jerry and Pink and the Brain.

From: Chappy Williams
To: Colin Jackson
Subject: Thank You

Thanks very much Colin,

I loved the Tom and Jerry joke! The story is all filed and I think it is very funny.

I hope you and Bob enjoy it,

All the best,
Chappy

From: Bob Servant
To: Colin Jackson
Subject: TOM AND FUCKING JERRY?

Colin,

What are you playing at?! Have you seen the Evening Telegraph?! What were you thinking? I never said anything about Tom and Jerry, I don't even like the bloody programme.

I've been getting absolute pelters all day. People keep giving it 'Ooh, Jerry, where's Colin?' And what's all this bollocks about you thinking I'm so handsome? We come across as a right couple of oddballs. By Christ, you've made me look like a complete idiot. Why the hell would I say that we're the new Tom and Jerry. What does that even mean, they were in a fucking cartoon for a start? I wouldn't know where to begin.

I am absolutely furious about this Colin.

Bob

Dundee Evening Telegraph

Broughty Ferry News   25·02·07

Filed 25.02.07 by Chappy Williams, Broughty Ferry Correspondent

WE'RE LIKE TOM AND JERRY, SAYS PAINTER ABOUT BROUGHTY FERRY MAN

An internationally known artist who has been commissioned by Broughty Ferry resident Bob Servant to produce a portrait has bizarrely claimed that the two of them are the 'new Tom and Jerry'.

Colin Jackson, an English painter who was inspired by his father to pick up the brush back in the 1990s, contacted Servant through the Internet and the two of them hit it off immediately.

'I am always pleased to read Bob's e-mails,' says Jackson, 'because he is usually interesting. Bob must have been a handsome young man, because from the recent pictures he sent me he still looks great, so you can imagine how good he would have been if he was younger?'

It was while e-mailing each other about the painting, which is to show Servant on board a ship called *Bob's Beauty* from his long career in the Merchant Navy, that Jackson claims the two of them decided that they could be the modern-day incarnation of Walt Disney's much loved cartoon duo.

'It was Bob's idea,' says Jackson. 'We both love Tom and Jerry, and he suggested that we could make ourselves like them. He said the world is crying out for a new Tom and Jerry and we would be perfect for the job. I'm not sure how we're going to make ourselves the new Tom and Jerry, because they were cartoon characters but, knowing Bob as I do, he'll have something up his sleeve!'

However, when contacted by the *Evening Telegraph* today, Servant claimed he had no knowledge of the Tom and Jerry plan. 'This is news to me,' he said from Doc Ferry's public bar.

From: Colin Jackson
To: Bob Servant
Subject: Re: TOM AND FUCKING JERRY?

Hello Bob,

Whats all this about? I only said I liked Tom and Jerry not you so I think your friend Williams should be confronted not me. So i don't see any reason why you should be harassing me like i am some kind of toy or something like that.

Colin

From: Bob Servant
To: Colin Jackson
Subject: I am sorry Colin but this is goodbye

Colin,

I have spoken to Chappy and he is sticking to his story. The last few days have been a complete nightmare and I have been turned into a laughing stock by the Tom and Jerry story. The local radio station had a phone-in yesterday on the matter and the resounding opinion was that I was a basket case.

A taxi driver phoned in from the Seagate rank in Dundee and said that he'd just seen me chasing a mouse down the road with a rubber hammer (which was untrue) and then a woman from Monifieth called and, sounding all pleased with herself, said, "Forget Walt Disney, I think Bob Servant's been on the Malt Whisky."

I knew things were bad when I nipped up to the bowling club and bumped into Jimmy Walker and Bill Wood. Jimmy went to shake my hand and then said, 'Hang on Bob, have you washed your paws?' Then Bill said that the bar was closed so would I be able to nip through the cat flap and get them a couple of drinks? They're both right good guys so when they have a pop you know you're in trouble.

I am sorry Colin but under the circumstances I cannot take the painting from you. I just want to forget about the whole matter. I do not hold any grudge against you, it's just one of those things. Best of luck for the future,

Yours,
Bob Servant

No Reply

Bob,

What's an acceptable amount of money to lend a family member? My brother's out of work but my wife says I shouldn't give him money because he boozes like a madman.

'Brotherly Love', Teddington

*****

Friend,

The fact that your brother boozes like a madman is exactly the reason you should give him money. One of the many qualities of the heavy drinker is how many ideas they have. The great irony, of course, is that these ideas often strike at the very worst time — when the boozer is laying with great dignity on the pavement, or sleeping on a bus, or berating themselves in an alleyway. And even if they're capable of remembering the idea, they often lack the means to act on it, having spent their meagre resources on much-needed refreshment, fast food and 'on the spot' fines from the constabulary. However, armed with your investment, your brother will put that money to use and you'll soon be rich beyond your wildest dreams and your boo-boy wife's tune will change with immediate effect. It's a win-win-win.

Yours,
Bob

~~~~~~~~~~~~

Bob,

You are clearly a very successful businessman. You don't get an extension like that if you don't know your way around a balance sheet. Could I trouble you for the secret of your success?

Bob Cryer, Hampshire

* * * * *

Dear Bob,

Being a businessman is a state of mind. I am, and let me put this as
simply as I can, a man who gets up every day and, without even trying,
finds himself sniffing out business opportunities like a German
Shepherd that has been trained by the police to sniff out business
opportunities rather than hard drugs such as heroin or LSD. I am a one-
man business ideas machine and I simply don't have an 'off' button.

In the early 1970s, I built a window-cleaning round that, according to
Frank and it's never been fully disproved, was briefly the largest
window-cleaning round in Western Europe. From then on it was venture
after venture until I became the renowned Cheeseburger Van operator
that I am today. Success in business is about having a good handshake,
knowing your way around a joke and, more than anything,
understanding the power of negotiation. Whatever business I have been
in over the years, whether it was the purchase of a lightly fire-damaged
ladder, or paying cash for an industrial-sized bin full of 'no questions
asked' meat of mixed origin from a night janitor at Dundee's once-great
Camperdown Zoo, I have become a master of the art of negotiation
which I take great pleasure in gifting to you, and indeed the nation,
right now,

Bob

"NEVER GIVE AN INCH"

Bob Servant's Four Point Guide to Successful Negotiation

1. Where-ever you meet the folk you are negotiating with, get there early and stick up topless photos of yourself doing sporty stuff. If they ask how the photos got there say the photos were already there when you arrived, you're genuinely embarrassed about them, but ultimately there's nothing you can do about it.

2. When the folk you are negotiating with make their opening offer, laugh for a minimum of three minutes.

3. During the negotiations, apologise and take an 'urgent phone call' from a man from the United Arab Emirates who is offering to 'blow the bidding out of the water'. I once did this to great effect while selling a pair of barely-used long johns to an impressionable milkman. We were sparring away at the £3 mark but when I took the call from 'the Middle-East's biggest Long John nut' I had the milkman almost literally in my pocket and we closed the deal at a cool £3.25.

4. Do not cry during a negotiation. If you do cry say that you are crying in happiness because you're so good at business but, in an ideal world, do not cry in a negotiation.

Dear Bob,

I'm applying for jobs and I get very nervous in interviews. Any advice?

Joe Coley, London

* * * * *

Dear Joe,

I strongly advise you to listen to my relaxation tape and let your worries melt away like a snowman in a sauna. Please send £9.99 by return of post[24].

Yours in hope,
Bob

---

[24] I found and transcribed this tape. I suspect the cover art was not done by a professional.

Bob Servant Relaxation Tape
Original Recording – December 2022
Transcribed by Neil Forsyth September 2023

Transcription Starts

Reggae music plays softly in background.

Bob: Let me take you on a journey. You're lying on a Caribbean beach covered in yellow sand. You've rubbed expensive sun tan lotion over every inch of your body apart from your eyes.

Frank: And your undercarriage.

Bob: I'm doing the talking, Frank.

Frank: Sorry.

Bob: All around you people laugh and drink Lilt straight out of the bottle. A frogman emerges from the water with a harpoon. He's caught an octopus, a dolphin and some smoked mackerel.

Frank: Not a bad day's work.

Bob: If you speak again, you'll wait in the van.

Frank: Sorry, Bob, I got sucked into the story.

(Sound of a deep breath)

Bob: You look out to sea. A fun-loving woman on water-skis is dragged through the waves. She shouts (voice becomes high-pitched) 'I'm having the most wonderful time!'

Frank: Can't blame her. Oh, Christ! Sorry, Bob.

(Sound of a deep breath)

Bob: Up in a palm tree is a very pretty seagull. It flies down and lands on your left breast. And the seagull says, 'Alright mate? Just relax, have fun and take it easy. Just take it easy, real easy.' Listen to the seagull. Listen to the seagull, (voice becomes faint) listen to the seagull...

(Tape continues)

Bob: Did you see Cash in The Attic today?

Frank: The roller skates?

Bob: How did they think they were going to get any money for roller skates?

Frank: God knows.

Bob: They're in la la land.

Frank: I think the tape's still running Bob.

Bob: Oh, for Christ's sake!

RECORDING ENDS

– 7 –

Deadeye the Fleet-footed Wonderboy

From: Chris Adams
To: Bob Servant
Subject: Can you help?

Dear Sir / Madam Please read.

It is my sincere pleasure at this moment to exhibit my total trust bestowed on you in accordance to my Proposed partnership relationship with you of which I am fully convinced that you will really welcome my partner. It is my Godly nursed intention to prove myself to you that I am very much different from others which you must have come across on the Internet.

The truth is that I am a dying man looking to invest funds abroad for the sake of my children and grandchildren. You are a business or invidividual that i have picked as a possible receiver of this investment. Simply return how much you would require and why i will consider how we can proceed. The money would come by banking transfer so let us save time by you providing full banking dretails on the form below.

1) Your Full Name........................... ...
2) Your Age............................ ....
3) Your Mobile and Home Phone Number..............
4) Your Fax Number.......................
5) Your Country of Nationality............................... .
6) Your Occupation.................... ....
7) Sex............................ ....
8) Alternative E-mail Address/ ....
I look forward for your immediate Positive response.
My regards to you and the family,
Mr Chris Adams

_____

From: Bob Servant
To: Chris Adams
Subject: Too Busy

Hello Chris,

Thanks for getting in touch and I'm sorry to hear that you're having a tough time. I'm afraid I can't help you right now as I am extremely busy. I feel like Santa on Christmas Eve or Dundee A&E on Christmas Day.[25]

I am Head Scout with a Scottish football team called Dundee United and I'm busy trying to find a star signing for the new season. We've lost a few players and the natives are restless. I need to pull something big out of my cat[26] here, Chris, a real Bobby Dazzler who can show the opposition a clean pair of heels and have the punters up on their tiptoes waving their rattles and with smiles as wide as the Clyde. I've got a bit of money to spend on the right player and, by God, I intend to get him.

Sorry Chris, I don't know why I'm telling you all this. You're busy with your health problems.

Best of luck for the future,

Your Servant,
Bob Servant

From: Chris Adams
To: Bob Servant
Subject: I know a star player

Bob,

In fact bob you are in most luck right now because I know a football soccer player like you will not believe. I can work on you with this if i was to introduce. Then of course you pay a fee. say $5000 as lump sum to be paid now? This player is one of the best that you will have seen. He has multiple experience and like you say will cause joy to the people. I myself have seen him play many times and in fact has been great comfort to me during illness to watch him play that is how much beautiful it is.

Chris

---

[25] See The Dundee Courier, 26 December 2010: 'Christmas Calamities' ('"All I'd ask him is 'Was it really worth it?' " said one middle-aged woman whose right foot had been crudely superglued to a turkey').
[26] Hat, presumably.

From: Bob Servant
To: Chris Adams
Subject: We don't pay agents

Chris,

That's a stroke of luck. Sorry we are not paying agents just now because of the cutbacks but I'm sure you'll want your friend to have his shot at glory and I'd imagine he'll chuck a few quid your way. Put it this way, he'll be getting a package like you wouldn't believe. We pay wages, expenses and a £50 a month boot polish allowance so I'm sure he'll bung you a fiver or two.

Yours,
Bob

From: Chris Adams
To: Bob Servant
Subject: I will pass this on

OK Bob I will pass you on and you can pay him money. Yes I will arrange with him. His name is Don Woodward and he will be in touch soon. I believe that he is even at training right now so this is a good sign for you Bob.

From: Don Woodward
To: Bob Servant
Subject: I am a striker with excellent experience

Dear Mr. Bob Servant The Chief player Scout

Good day Sir. I am pleased to write to inform you of my intention to ask that you give me an offer and a place in your Scottish football team of DUNDEE UNITED. I was given your details by one of my fans CHRIS ADAMS.

well what to say. I will keep short for now. I am a striker with excellent experience, young, strong & have good pace, very skillful and intelligent on the ball. It would be quite right for me to have a place at your football club. I have played for a number of top professional club here in Africa including leage champions and cup winner. I am happy to come and play for your team overe in Scotland and this is fine. I wil have to arrange release here and then there are all the costs to come to you and this will be quite high.

So let us arrange a deal and soon i will be there playing for you with all my heart Bob

thank you and pleased to meet you bob

DON WOODWARD
Football Player. Position: Forward

From: Bob Servant
To: Don Woodward
Subject: You're ticking my boxes

Don,

Thanks for getting in touch. You sound like a strong possibility. One slight hitch is that I've just had a wee look online for your name and could not find it anywhere. Considering the fact that you've played for league champions, that made my eyebrows take off like helicopters.

I presume you can clear this up easily enough? I certainly hope so. The fans want a star signing and there's a really terrible atmosphere around the place. I've not seen Dundee like this since the Timex strike which was a bad time for the city. Well, to be fair, it was a pretty good time for me.[27]

Your Servant
Bob Servant
Chief Scout

From: Don Woodward
To: Bob Servant
Subject: Not Important

Dear Mr. Bob Chief Scout

Do not worry bob not all teams and leagues here bother to post their news on internet why would they? Most fans know of the teams and players through word of mouth and this is how you have come to hear of me so you are in fact the evidence against yourself.

If you need more information then you should just come and ask me bob instead of wasting your time on the computer. You should know that I am 18 years old and am well built, very strong in air and very good on fifty fifty balls. I have speed and can beat defenders very easily and score with the help of my inborn speed. Also i am very skillful and intelligent on the ball. My position is forward, in my previous club i play as the top striker and due get result for my team. I am 6 foot 3 tall.

Regards
Don Woodward
Football Player. Position: Forward

---

[27] The Timex Strike of 1993 thrust Dundee into the national consciousness. When the Timex company brought in 'scab' labour to break the strike there was the worst picket-line violence seen in Britain since the 1984 miners' strike. As Bob said, however, not everyone in the city suffered during the strike. See The Dundee Courier, 10 January 1993: 'Dundee Cheese Burger Van Mogul Defends Timex Relocation' ('"I greatly admire the strikers and I am here to help," said Servant who has been selling large quantities of fast food to the crowd outside the factory gates. Servant pointed out that he has incurred significant costs "rebranding" his van. He now offers the "Scargill Sandwich" (a cheeseburger), the "Bolshevik Burger" (a cheeseburger) and "Stalin's Surprise" (also a cheeseburger). Servant went on to defend his offer of high-interest credit to the strikers which he is marketing under the banner "Bash the Scabs, Start a Tab!"').

From: Bob Servant
To: Don Woodward
Subject: Your New Name

Don,

Wasting time on the computer is one thing that I hope no one can ever accuse me of. Things are looking good. The first thing I need to do, of course, is give you a new name. It is absolutely vital over here that any star player we have is given a name that will have the fans giving it laldy on their way to the ground and then waving their scarves like lunatics when you take to the grass. Some of our old heroes here at United had great names. I'm thinking, as you'll know, of boys like Slippers Malpas, Angel Toes Bannon, Put Away The Cigar Milne and old 'Magic Socks' himself - Trickshot Narey The Man Who Made Physics Cry.

Anyway, I've had a think and this is what I want to call you:

Deadeye the Fleet-footed Wonderboy

OK with you? Thanks for all the information. Can I just check on things like diet and personality? Tell me a little about the real Deadeye.

Bob

From: Don Woodward
To: Bob Servant
Subject: Name OK

Dear Mr. Bob Servant

Thanks once again for you communication. OK i understand this with the name and this is fine to call me. It is also correct as i am fleet foot for sure. Bob i run like you will not believe. I like your picture and i hope i can play as well as these famous names.

Regarding my character, i am humble and only concentrate on my football carrier. I like listening to soft music and most of the American gospels Music. Gospel songs is my daily bread that give me lots of inspiration in my career. For diet I take lite food in the morning after training and rice for my evening meals. So it is good we are nearly in agreement. can we start to arrange our deal now bob? i do not like to talk of these things i rather talk only of football but the business must be done so let us carry on.

From Don, or for you it is DEADEYE!

From: Bob Servant
To: Don Woodward
Subject: Some action shots?

Deadeye,

I'm delighted to hear about the Gospel music and the rice, which is the kind of combo I was hoping you'd come up with. It's time that I saw Deadeye in action. Can you send some photos from your latest training session please?

I have a hunch, and right now it's only a hunch, that you are both my kind of player and, more importantly, my kind of man. You've really come up with the goods for me, like Nick Owen did when Sir Trevor McDonald poisoned that bus driver.[28]

Bob
Chief Scout

From: Don Woodward
To: Bob Servant
Subject: photos from training time

Bob

Thank you Bob I will never let you down when I play for you and i will never forget that you talk of me like this. I see this as respect between men and I will repay you for sure when I am on the pitch in fact i dedicate my first game to you and your family because of all you have done for me.

You want photos so i have sent some now from my training and they show well my capabties for you. You should know my TRAINING SCHEDULE:- I do Gym on Saturdays evening but i train twice everyday from Monday–Friday. I like Physical training on Monday morning and lite ball work on Monday evening. I go to church on Sundays so no training. You should know that I play very similar to famous play Samuel etc. I play both legs but very perfect with my rite leg. Can we now go to the business side?

Regards
Your DEADEYE

---

[28] The former television newsreader Sir Trevor McDonald has never poisoned a bus driver. He did, however, beat a homeless man to death in Birmingham in 1991. See *Your Headlines Tonight: The Trevor McDonald Story* p.201 ('"Any change, Sir Trevor?" he asked. I looked around me. We were alone. I walked over and said, "I will give you some change, by God I will give you some change." When I came to my senses he was dead and my suit was beyond repair. I felt sick. I called Nick Owen who walked off the 12th green at Sunningdale and incurred a speeding ticket on the M25 in his rush to help me. We buried the body at sea, on high tide at Holy Island. The sight of Nick Owen's head framed against the breaking dawn while he weighted down the body with his golf clubs was one of the most beautiful sights I have ever seen. Afterwards we went for a cooked breakfast and, despite his protestations, I reimbursed Nick for his golf clubs and we went halves on the speeding ticket. It was simply the right thing to do').

From: Bob Servant
To: Don Woodward
Subject: Great Photos

Deadeye,

Thanks for the photos which are great if a little confusing. Firstly you seem to have undergone quite a transformation between the two photos? Also, did you not say you were eighteen years old? Fuck me, Deadeye, what was your paper round, the entire Sahara? You're the oldest kid since Krankie.

Bob

From: Don Woodward
To: Bob Servant
Subject: RE: Great Photos

Bob,

My hair has changed between photos and that is all. Yes I am older for my age and this works only to your advantage bob as you will be surprised at my strength. Ok bob time to arrange deal. I have quickly worked out flight and everything, luggage and things like this, then insurance and also equipment and say first week of payment in advance. So bob shall we say $12,000 to get my account started and have me come to you? You need to show you are honest now Bob because sometimes you speak as if you are not,

DEADEYE

From: Bob Servant
To: Don Woodward
Subject: Celebration

Deadeye,

That all makes perfect sense. OK we are very nearly there now. I just need to know how you celebrate a goal? As our star signing you will be expected not only to score goals but also to celebrate them in a way that will have tongues wagging from Perth to Carnoustie. How will you, Deadeye The Fleet Footed Wonderboy, wag those tongues? Because I want you to wag them so hard, that you start a tsunami.

And please do not accuse me of not being honest, Deadeye. I would rather cut off my head than lie to you.

Your pal in the bootroom,

Bob

From: Don Woodward
To: Bob Servant
Subject: My celebrations for you

Bob,

This is the last question i will answer to you bob because it is too long now. if you to sign me be fast and also bob this is not right a player like me who has won legue titles should be here to sell himself like the women in the market sell the crayfish.

Ok last answer. When ever I score a goal my state of mind changed and i will be very exited and may be force to run to any angle of the pitch racing my hands and thanking God who give me the opportunity to score. As a striker the only thing that I know that will make the fans exited is scoring goals, when a player is a goal scorer he makes the fans happy and gain the support of the fans which will encourage him to work harder and score more goals for his team.

Right bob i attach full details for the bank transfer. Send $12000 now and then this will be sealed. You are sometimes talking as if not serious for this bob. Let us finish the business and have me there with you making fans happy.

Don and DEADEYE

From: Bob Servant
To: Don Woodward
Subject: I think we can do better than that

Deadeye,

Thanks for getting back to me and I wouldn't dream of treating you like a crayfish. I have to say though that your celebration didn't really grab my imagination. I have had a wee think and come up with an alternative:

GOAL CELEBRATION FOR DEADEYE THE FLEET FOOTED WONDERBOY

For a couple of seconds after the goal just stand there as if you can't believe what's happened, then explode into life.

Run as fast as you can to the away fans and cup your ear as if to say 'You were saying?' Then go down on one knee and pretend to bowl a bowling ball.

Run as fast as you can to the St John's Ambulance mob. Stand in front of them and pretend to have a heart attack then jump back to your feet and laugh as if to say 'Not on my watch'.

Run as fast as you can over to a ballboy and ruffle his hair until he laughs then gradually increase how hard you are ruffling his hair until he is on the verge of tears then stop ruffling his hair, pick him up and scream in his ear 'You are the naughtiest boy in Britain'.

Run as fast as you can to the fire exit in the corner of the pitch and out to the street.

Run as fast as you can down Tannadice Street, take a right on Arklay Street and stop at the bus stop on the corner of Dens Road. The bus you want is the number 75 to Broughty Ferry. Take a window seat on the right-hand side of the bus so you get a nice view of the river.

Get off the bus at Broughty Ferry train station and run as fast as you can to Harbour View Road. My house is the one with the Space Age extension. Let yourself in. I'll be asleep in the big armchair with Zulu on the telly with the sound down. Kneel down and wake me up by slowly circling my temples with your fingers. It's possible I'll say something like 'not so firm, Frank'. If so, ignore it and certainly don't read anything into it.

When I wake up, look at me with that wonky little smile of yours and say, 'I did it boss. I popped one in the onion bag'.

We'll just ad lib it from there. One thing though, Deadeye, please don't take off your shirt off at any point or you'd be in danger of receiving a yellow card.

NO REPLY

Dear Bob,

I'm sick of being skint. As a successful businessman can you tell me how to earn the big bucks?

'Empty Pockets', Burnley

* * * * *

Friend,

I'll never forget my friend Tommy Peanuts telling me an intriguing theory about money. He explained that money is an energy. If you want to have it, then simply close your eyes and 'invite' that energy to come into your life. I found that fascinating. Tommy lost his house a few weeks later.

Yours in hope,
Bob

Bob,

I met my fiancée's brother for the first time last night. Before we'd got our starters he'd shown me a photo of his car and told me how much he earns. What's my next move?

'Greatly Concerned', Birmingham

* * * * *

Friend,

Ask for the ring back and get on with your life.

Yours in hope,

Bob

Bob,

My mother has been leering at my new boyfriend a bit, especially
when she's been on the gin (so pretty much always). He's a good-
looking man but it's getting ridiculous. How do I get her to wind it
in?

'Uncomfortable', Glasgow

*****

Dear friend,

I feel for him because I've been wrestling with this kind of thing for
years. I try not to be in the vicinity of hen parties, for example, or my
clothes will be shredded from my body within seconds and, if not
physically stopped, they'll start nibbling at my flesh like eels. In the end I
have had to wear a specially adapted outfit whenever I am in a crowded
area, or it just gets out of hand (photo enclosed). I suggest your
boyfriend adopts something similar for future family gatherings.

Yours in hope,

Bob

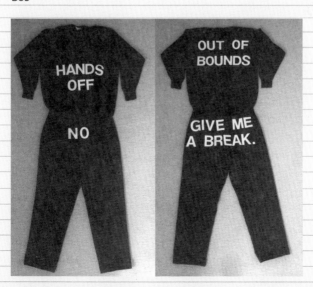

– 8 –

The Church of Broughty Ferry

From: James Joseph
To: Bob Servant
Subject: Good Day

Dear Sir,

Good day to you. I got your letter forwarded to me, which you received from my in law Dr Bakayoko Ahmed who is currently at Spain on a business trip. I hope you are the rightful person because Dr Bakayoko Ahmed, informed me concerning you and the $1,5m. OK I need your full names and contact address with your telephone number. I shall then arrange payment of the money $1,5m to you. Try and get back to me with this information as quick as possible. I am still in the office.

Regards,
Mr James Joseph

From: Bob Servant
To: James Joseph
Subject: Can't Place Him...

Hi James,

Thanks for getting in touch but I'm afraid I just can't place Dr Bakayoko Ahmed and I'm pretty sure I'd remember a name like that. I live in Broughty Ferry, Dundee and round here it's all Mikes, Shuggys and Engelberts.[29]

Sorry I couldn't be of more help,

Your Servant,
Bob Servant

---

[29] See The Dundee Courier 15 July 2011: 'Singer "Mystified and Humbled" by Dundee Baby-naming Statistics.'

From: James Joseph
To: Bob Servant
Subject: Good Day

Dear Mr Bob Servant,

Bob I have checked over this with Dr Bakayoko Ahmed and he has confirmed that it is you who he wanted to receive this money. It is possible you met him a long time ago but do not worry about this the most important is to arrange transit of this money to you so please provide the data. Bob please don't miss this money because of one thing or the other because I know nothing good comes so easily your miracles has come!

I wait for your reply.

Regards
Mr James Joseph

From: Bob Servant
To: James Joseph
Subject: Fair enough

James,

Right, well that's fine then. I am 64 years old and have lived a life like you wouldn't believe, James, so there's no doubt I could have bumped into Dr Bakayoko and forgotten about it. I probably had a chat with him in Safeways or bought a toaster off him through the small ads. I'm just glad I made enough of an impression on the big man for him to think of me for this windfall. I feel like that wee boy when Willie Wonka made him put on gold underpants and go with him to the disco.[30]

Sorry to hear about your leg by the way.
Bob

From: James Joseph
To: Bob Servant
Subject: Good Day

Bob,

What is this about my leg? There is no problem with my leg at all Bob. Thank you very much for your mail. I hope you are interested to receive your fund if your answer is yes then lets us do everything this week so that you can receive your fund this week because time waits for no body.

Regards,
Mr James Joseph

---

[30] A pretty confused rendition from Bob of the opening section of Willie Wonka and the Chocolate Factory. The 'wee boy' was the 10-year-old character Charlie Bucket who chanced upon the golden wrapping of a chocolate bar and as a result was granted access to the aforementioned chocolate factory. At no point in the film was Charlie shown wearing gold underpants and he was certainly not pressurised by Wonka into putting some on. Neither, for that matter, did the two of them visit a disco.

From: Bob Servant
To: James Joseph
Subject: A quick check?

James,

A friend who shall remain nameless (my neighbour Frank) told me you were having terrible problems with your left leg. Can you give it a quick check? Would be good to put this one to bed.

Yours,
Bob

From: James Joseph
To: Bob Servant
Subject: Good Day

Bob,

Of course i would know any problem with my own leg and no there is none your firend has this all wrong. let us talk business now?

James

From: Bob Servant
To: James Joseph
Subject: I am so sorry

James,

My deepest apologies. I don't know what got into Frank's mind. I am mortified about this blunder and I can only hold up my hands and apologise. I just hope that you can forgive me and follow the 'British Way' when it comes to forgiving mistakes. I remember, for example, when Prince Charles admitted to having sex with a cactus.[31] It was a case of holding his hands up, saying, 'boys will be boys' and everyone moving on. That's the British Way, James. People make mistakes so please just let it go and don't be a nob about it.

Yours for Blighty,
Bob

---

[31] The now King Charles has never admitted to having sex with a cactus and nor should he.

From: James Joseph
To: Bob Servant
Subject: No problem Bob

Sir,

I will not hold mistake against you becuse it is your friend Frank who got it wrong and you were just gving right concern about it all. Now this is not what is important to us Mr bob let us work on in good faith now after this soon as you let me know how you want to receeve your fund I promise you in the next ten working days everything is then concluded OK.

Your friend
James

From: Bob Servant
To: James Joseph
Subject: Start the bus

It would be good to know a bit more about each other? I'll start. I live here in Dundee and made a pile in the windowcleaning and cheeseburger van games and now spend my time checking my respect levels in the once great pubs of Broughty Ferry. Please tell me a bit about yourself.

From: James Joseph
To: Bob Servant
Subject: Good Day

Dear Mr Bob Servant,

Thank you for telling me of your life and yes I will tell you of mine. Mr. Bob, I am 60 years older man and a pastor in redeem Christian church of God Nigeria. I have been a pastor for more than 25 years since my life I have been working for God and my wife is also a pastor assisting me
I have never traveled out of Nigeria before but I believe one day I wilt travel may be to visit you in your country. Now about the transaction you have to tell me the way you want to receive the fund the bank has three options.

{1} BANK TO BANK WIRE TRANSFER
{2} THROUGH INTERNATIONAL BANK DRAFT.
{3} THROUGH INTERNATIONAL DEBIT CARD {ATM}

If you let me know any of this option I will let the bank know and within 10 working days the transaction will be concluded and you will have your money with you. Let me hear from you.

Regards
Mr James Joseph

From: Bob Servant
To: James Joseph
Subject: You're in the God mob?

James,

You have no idea how happy you have made me by telling me that you are a pastor.

James, I am a God man. I'm all over the guy, reading about the stuff he's done turns my heart into jelly and my eyebrows into chopsticks.

The problem is that I come from Dundee. It's not a religious place, James. The men are like wild animals and the women are worse. Ever since I found God I have been trying to get other people to join me without luck. The only religious guy I know in Dundee is that mad baker up in Clepington Road[32] but he's away with it. Sometimes I feel like the only man in Dundee who will admit to having a wee 'pal in the sky'.

To cut a long story short I'm going to have a crack at starting my own church and you sound like just the man to help me. As I said, I'm worth a few quid and would be willing to make a donation to your church if you allow me the honour of making you Chief Spiritual Adviser for what I have decided will be called the 'Church of Broughty Ferry'?

Yours in God and Jesus,
Bob

From: James Joseph
To: Bob Servant
Subject: Yes I will help you Bob

Dear Mr. Bob Servant,

Thank you very much Mr. Bob, am happy to read from you again and ready to do what ever you ask me to do in the name of God. Please let me know how we can start because I am ready to give you all the support you want since it is the work of our lord Jesus Christ. I wait to hear from you and yes a donation would be right.

Regards
Mr James Joseph

---

[32] See Dundee Yellow Pages, p.26, Bakeries, 'A Pie for A Pie', 176 Clepington Road (closed Sundays).

From: Bob Servant
To: James Joseph
Subject: Let's Do It!

James,

That's terrific. Right well let's plan for this Sunday then for the first meeting of the Church of Broughty Ferry. I'd better start hunting for a suitable location. What does a church need please, James? I've seen them on Songs of Praise but I know that's all CGI.[33] And how can I get people along on Sunday? Give me some bait for my Jesus hook.

As it says in the bible, 'You will meet a tall, dark stranger'. Well, I think I've met mine! Welcome aboard, James.

Bob Servant
Minister, Priest and Social Secretary
The Church of Broughty Ferry

From: James Joseph
To: Bob Servant
Subject: My advice

Hello Bob,

I do not think it says this in the bible but do not worry on this. Yes this Sunday will be best Bob that is the day when God is most close. Bob, you can go and look for a building that has an open space that will contain at least 300 to 500 population. It must be near the commercial centre to attract the people. Bob I think people I in scottland will know God from you soon and this to to be success.

Mr. Bob for this donation I sugest that i am going to send you some of the living bible books to empower you so that you will know what to tell your congregations. I want this book to get to your door step at least by Sunday morning. This books will cost you $120 only, and you will get as many as 30 of this books to realy equip you in your ministry over there in your country for you to understand the bilble and how to apply the principle on it.

This the information to send the money.

NAME. REV. JAMES JOSEPH.
ADDRESS; LAGOS NIGERIA.
AMOUNT; $120 ONLY.
TEXT QUATIONS; BIBLE
TEXT ANSWER; CHURCH.

Rev. James Joseph.
N/B; jESUS IS LORD!

---

[33] Some of the things that Bob has described to me as being 'all CGI': hovercrafts, the Grand National, the Eiffel Tower, the TV advertising campaigns of Domino's Pizza and the television presenter Eamonn Holmes.

From: Bob Servant
To: James Joseph
Subject: Call off the search we have a church

Hi James,

The books sound like a good idea, put me down for 10 copies for now. We have found our church! I took your advice that it has to be near the commercial centre. The good news is that I found a building, the bad news is that it's the public toilet.

A couple of years ago Dundee City Council passed a law that everyone had to have a toilet in their house. Apart from a few conscientious objectors most folk got on board so the public toilet doesn't really see much action these days. The only person that uses it is Slim Smith. I don't know if you know much about Slim Smith but he's roughly the size, and indeed shape, of a two-man tent. But Slim has promised me he's not going to be in town on Sunday so we're welcome to use the toilet for our church.

The toilet itself is quite small. I was thinking that I'll put a plank over the sinks and stand up there, and the urinals could be a religious water feature. There's a nice high roof and with the tiling the hymns should sound wonderful.

As it says in the bible 'You don't have to be mad to work here, but it helps!!!!'

Photo of the Church attached, it needs a wee tidy but as I said it ticks all the boxes.

Bob Servant
Head Honcho
The Church of Broughty Ferry

From: James Joseph
To: Bob Servant
Subject: You must buy bibles

Bob

Yes like yo say you must tidy up this room properly for use Sunday. This is good that there is to be a church but be careful about the toilet because God name must always be used in place with respect. There is no mention of this being mad situation in bible Bob you are saying it wrong again. you might have different bible to me. that is why you buy must books from me to make sure you are equip with right bible for the scottland people.

remember about the books. If i can have the money today i believe you can get the parcel at your doorstep first thing monday morning through Express courier services DHL. You have all payment detail.

Rev. James Joseph

From: Bob Servant
To: James Joseph
Subject: Up to four!

Hi James,

Things are heating up here ahead of tomorrow's first congregation of the Church of Broughty Ferry. I'm very pleased to say I have three confirmed guests. They are:

My neighbour and best pal Frank. Frank used to work for me on the windowcleaning and the burger vans so I suppose you can say he's been a disciple for a few years. He's Judassed me on a few occasions, but I think we can trust him, James, and I'm giving him the vice-captain position.

Tommy Peanuts. Tommy's an old pal of mine and he's struggling to come to terms with his divorce from his wife, who ran off with Woof McKee, the dog kennels tycoon from Arbroath. I thought he should come along and hear what God has to say about things.

Shirley McHugh. An elderly but largely fun-loving woman from Monifieth who is medically blind but we had a good chat and she's keen as mustard so I invited her along.

I know it's not the best turnout in the world James but, as it says in the bible, 'three's a crowd'.

I need to get this sermon written for tomorrow,

Bob

From: James Joseph
To: Bob Servant
Subject: Bibles

Bob

You did not even mention bibles i have them heer for you all agreed?
Wheers is the money for these book bob you promised are you not religous man
like you said? you show again that you are using the wrong bible with these
words

Yes three people is ok for now – out of seeds grow bigger plants bob this is
what to remember. A sermon is always needed of course best to speak to people
hearts bob and have them find connection of their own with God.

Send money for bibles and i can have them rush job to you DHL

James

From: Bob Servant
To: James Joseph
Subject: The Sermon

Hi James,

OK I've had a shot at the sermon and I am very proud to send you the
attached. I hope you like it because I think it presses all the right buttons. As
Jesus says in the bible 'I'm happy as Larry'.

That's me off to bed ahead of the big day tomorrow. I will dream of Jesus
(not in a saucy way). I hope you have a good night. May God be with you
(not in a saucy way).

Bob

THE CHURCH OF BROUGHTY FERRY
OPENING SERMON BY PASTOR BOB SERVANT,
'THE PEOPLE'S PASTOR'

Ladies and Gentlemen, thank you for coming to the
debut congregation of the 'all new' Church of
Broughty Ferry. You know, a lot of people ask me
about God. They ask about who he is and what he
wants. Well, let me tell you this. God is a man who
has seen it all. He has heard every joke, told
every story and spent time with some of the most
interesting people in the world. To keep it simple,
God is like Nelson Mandela or the former Grandstand
presenter Bob Wilson.

Bob Wilson, ladies and gentlemen, wasn't a trained
television presenter and a lot of people forget
that. He was a goalie and a pretty decent one as
well. He played for Scotland but I think he only
got one cap. I can't remember. But when he hung up
the gloves Bob Wilson didn't spend his time
swaggering round the golf club or acting the big
shot at the swimming baths. No, Bob Wilson got the
bus to the BBC, picked up a microphone and said
'Can I have a wee shot at this lads?' And the rest
is history.

Like Bob Wilson, God is the man of many jobs. He
helps people with problems, he stops wars and he
makes sure that everyone in the world gets their
dinner. And just when he thought he couldn't do any
more, God had sex with Mary and produced the twins
— Joseph and Jesus. Those twins were not just two
adorable wee lads, which they were, they also went
about the business of telling people about God and
not in a 'Oh you should see my Dad he's a cowboy
during the week and an astronaut at the weekend'
sort of way. But in a 'my Dad's God, beat that'
sort of way which was fair enough and not as

arrogant as it might sound. When Joseph retired and
Jesus was murdered by the Nazis, God had a wee cry,
shook himself down and kept going and he's still
going strong today.

A lot of people ask me how old God is. I tell them
to think of the biggest number they know then
double it and add 32 and that's not how old God is,
that's how old his NEWEST pair of trainers are. God
is the oldest man in the world and, as long as he
stays alive, it's going to be very hard for anyone
to nick that title off him. And here's the twist,
if someone did become older than him, then God
would be the first boy at their door with a
chocolate orange and a birthday card because that's
the kind of boy he is. He's a nice guy, that's what
I'm saying, ladies and gentlemen, more than
anything, God is a nice guy. Nicer than anyone you
know. He's nicer than Gloria Hunniford and, yes,
he's nicer than the Pope who, let's not forget,
works for Go. If God is a newsagent, and a lot of
people say he is, then the Pope is God's paperboy.

Ladies and Gentlemen, thank you for listening and
let me leave you with this. Who made those clothes
you are wearing? The cardigans, the duffel coats
and the underpants? Don't read the label. Read your
hearts. Because your clothes, ladies and gentlemen,
were made by God and he didn't even tell you. That
is the kind of guy he is. Good morning, ladies and
gentlemen. Follow God's path and watch the step on
the way out because Frank tripped on it the other
day and went down like the Belgrano.

Good afternoon ladies and gentlemen. Hallelujah!
See you in heaven. I love you. Come back next week,
there will be a collection for those who can afford
it. good night and Amen.

(APPLAUSE)

Page 2

From: James Joseph
To: Bob Servant
Subject: Sermon OK

Bob this is all fine you talk well off god tho maybe it is little confusing with the other people but god is there and this is fine and yes it is right for hallejulahg and to end everything with the AMEN.

It is Sunday now bob and you have not bought the bibles so this is very rong and you musst know this too bob. ok well let us say the bibbles will be with you next week and then you will be ready to go through with the second meeting of your new CHURCH.

Good luck today bob let me kno if the great sucess i know it will be and then you can send the money for the bibles OK Bob.

GOOD LUCK
Rev. James Joseph

From: Bob Servant
To: James Joseph
Subject: I'm Having Doubts

James,

Well, where to begin? It's fair to say that the Church of Broughty Ferry didn't go exactly as you and I had hoped. It started not too bad. Tommy, Frank and Shirley all showed up and I stood outside the toilet and welcomed them with a bit of a pat on the back and some of the 'God Be With You' stuff. I made a wee joke about the steps up to the toilet being our 'Stairway to Heaven' and the atmosphere was pretty decent when I climbed up onto the taps for the sermon.

Unfortunately I had just started my speech when Slim Smith came into the toilet. He didn't say anything and none of the others saw him. He just shook his head and went straight into a cubicle. I was knocked off my stride but for a moment it seemed like we'd get away it.

Then he started. James, the noises that Slim made were simply inhumane. What came out of that cubicle sounded like a drunken brass band. Unfortunately at the first blast from the cubicle Shirley thought it was the opening note of Onward Christian Soldiers and started singing away, which got Frank started. They barely knew the words so trying to match their singing up to Slim's 'tune' was a tough job for them. Then Tommy Peanuts started crying which I thought was because of his divorce but was actually because he was standing nearest the cubicle.

In the end I had to climb down from the sinks and lead the congregation outside. Shirley said I should sack my organist, Tommy went to drown his sorrows and me and Frank waited for Slim. He finally came out looking very sorry for himself and said he'd had an entire pork belly for breakfast. Frank tried to lighten the mood by saying that at least Slim had 'made a donation' but I told Frank it was not a laughing matter and walked away with my head held high but my heart feeling like a lava lamp.

That's me back at the house now, James, and I just don't know what to say. What kind of God would allow this to happen? What kind of God would convince Slim Smith to eat an entire pork belly for breakfast? I just don't know any more, James. I'm wondering that maybe there is no God after all and we've both been duped?

Yours In Doubt,
Bob

From: James Joseph
To: Bob Servant
Subject: RE: I'm Having Doubts

Bob I start to think you are for joking because this is just too extreme now. a man went to the toilet in the church and this made a man cry and everything go bust? Come on bob this is not right it cannot be for true.

If you are real and this is what you are really doing in scottland then show me by sending the money today for your books and do not let me down bob because i already have the books from the printers and they are packed and all ready nice for you

James

From: Bob Servant
To: James Joseph
Subject: Hold Tight!

James,

I was having breakfast and I think God and Jesus sent me a message. Thoughts?

Yours in Hope,
Bob

NO REPLY

Bob,

I have a rather pronounced nose. How do I minimise any negative effect with the ladies?

Deek McDonnell, Hackney

* * * * *

Friend,

Thanks for your letter Deek, or should I say Beak? Just my little joke, Deek, don't be a fanny about it. With regards to your conk situation, it's all about ownership. By addressing the situation head on (pun intended) you can quickly dilute the impact of your massive sniffer. The next time you go for a date, get a friend to come to the bar wearing a very large false nose and position themselves nearby. To the girl you're with, the looming presence of your friend's 'nose' will reduce your nose down to normal size. That is probably, and I do not say this lightly, one of my best ever ideas. The very best of luck to you, God 'nose' you'll need it.

Yours in hope,

Bob

~~~~~~~~~~~~~~~~

Dear Bob,

Got my Great-Aunt Janet's funeral on Saturday. I've had to cancel playing five-a-side beforehand. I could have probably managed both but I would have been in my Adidas Sambas at the funeral and my wife said that would have been out of order. Anyway, I'm not sure how to play it at the funeral. All I remember about Janet is that she liked Coronation Street and wore the least convincing wig in Glasgow.

Yours respectfully
Bingo McKenzie, Glasgow

* * * * *

Bingo,

Despite spending the majority of her time pie-eyed on supermarket gin (an educated guess), your wife is right on this occasion. You need to hang up your Sambas and concentrate on giving Janet the send-off she deserves by attending the funeral in costume as filthy-minded Coronation Street legend Vera Duckworth. Use her 'Ooh, ducky!' catchphrase liberally upon arrival, and when the coffin begins its descent, call out, 'Ooh, down she goes, and not for the first time!' and let loose with one of Vera's much-loved cackles. It's the kind of bawdy observation that Janet would have loved and the other punters at the funeral will howl with laughter. Who knows, maybe inside the coffin Janet will have a last wee chuckle herself? Fingers crossed!

Good luck and RIP,

Bob

* * * * *

Bob,

That all sounds great. I'm sourcing the Vera outfit from charity shops. Can I ask for a couple more tips on the funeral? It's my first one apart from when we buried my uncle's cat Horatio, but that was a pretty informal affair. Do I tip the minister?

Bingo

* * * * *

Bingo,

Please find enclosed my full Funeral Etiquette Guide. Please send £5.99 by return of post[34].

Yours,

Bob

---

[34] Over the years, for unclear reasons, Bob has produced a wide range of etiquette guides. Distribution has been disappointing.

"Abide With Glee"
Bob Servant's
Guide to Funerals

1 Stand out

If you want to be a big hit at the funeral,
you need to swim against the tide. Every
man and his dog will be muttering about
the deceased being a decent man or
woman, and how they only killed their
own, and so on. Grab attention by saying
you thought they were 'the absolute pits'
and how you're only there for the
sandwiches. People will admire your no-
nonsense attitude and give you an unholy
amount of respect.

2. Seating

Often the deceased's family go out of their way to grab the best seats at a funeral. Get round their selfishness by taking your own deckchair and setting up shop at the front.

3. The minister/priest /rabbi/sheikh/ sensei

Get the main man/woman on your side early doors by clapping above your head whenever they finish talking. When they finish their big speech, spray them all over with mid-range champagne. They'll feel like a famous Formula One driver and be forever in your debt.

4. The singing

When it comes to the hymns, there's always someone with a deep voice who arrogantly dominates proceedings. The easiest, and classiest, way around that is to take along a microphone and small portable speaker.

5. Cheering up the punters

People are sad at funerals and it's your job to cheer them up (no one else is going to do it!). You can do some low-level stuff outside the church – hand buzzers, 'finding' money behind ears – but once the service starts you can really get going. One way to turn the punters' 'tears into wine' is to wait until the coffin is on its way into the fire, throw a string of sausages on top of it and say you might as well 'cook some bangers for the wake'. It's a fun, visual joke that will have the punters clapping like seals.

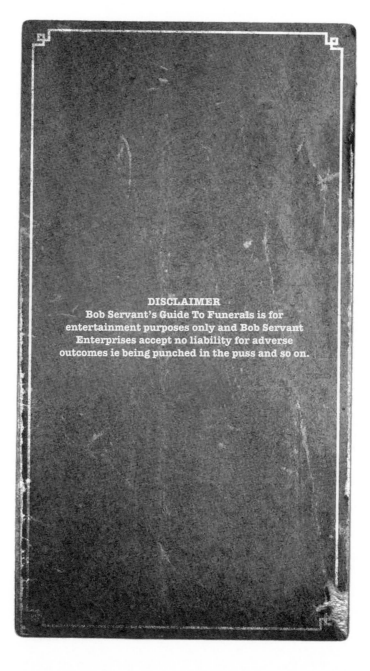

DISCLAIMER
Bob Servant's Guide To Funerals is for
entertainment purposes only and Bob Servant
Enterprises accept no liability for adverse
outcomes ie being punched in the puss and so on.

Bob,

That all makes perfect sense. I was surprised you didn't talk about what to wear. Surely I can't go to every funeral dressed as Vera Duckworth?

Bingo

* * * * *

Bingo,

Don't be ridiculous. For normal funerals just wear something appropriate. I wear the attached. It's dignified, chic and sends the relevant messages.

Best wishes,

Bob

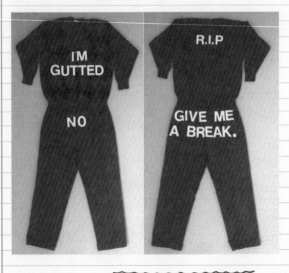

– 9 –

From Lanzhou to Willy's Chinese Palace

From: LANZHOU GLOBAL LTD
To: Bob Servant
Subject: JOB OPPORTUNITY/ MAKE MORE INCOME

Dear Sir/Madam,

We are Lanzhou Global, a specialist in the production of Rubber belts such as power transmission belts, conveyor belts etc. We have reached big sales volume of rubber products in USA/Canada and now trying to penetrate the United Kingdom and European market. Quite soon we shall open representative offices in the United Kingdom and therefore we are looking for people to assist us.

We need agents to receive payment in bank wire transfers and to resend the money to us. You earn 10% from each operation and work as an independent contractor right from your home office. Your job is absolutely legal. You can earn up to 3000–4000 pounds monthly.

Best Regards,
Admin/Human Resources Manager, Xiong Li.

From: Bob Servant
To: LANZHOU GLOBAL LTD
Subject: OK, let's talk

Hello there

This looks very interesting indeed. My name is Bob Servant and I am a semi-retired Burger Van legend. How would I go about applying for this job?

Your Servant,
Bob Servant

From: LANZHOU GLOBAL LTD
To: Bob Servant
Subject: JOB OPPORTUNITY/ MAKE MORE INCOME

Dear Bob,

Thanks for responding to our offer. We are pleased with your interest. We are looking to extend our business to United Kingdom and have been facing difficulties in handling payments from our client, that is why we have decided to employ people over there whom we can trust. Do you understand our aims OK? Do not hesitate to ask any question.

XIONG LI

From: Bob Servant
To: LANZHOU GLOBAL LTD
Subject: MY GARAGE COULD BE AN OFFICE

Xiong,

I am very interested in working for your company. I have a big garage that I do not use much and I was thinking that I could convert it into an office? There isn't much in the garage – just a bike, a barbecue and around 36,000 jazz mags.

Many thanks,
Bob

PS What would be my job title?
PPS Is there a uniform?

From: LANZHOU GLOBAL LTD
To: Bob Servant
Subject: Re: MY GARAGE COULD BE AN OFFICE

Hello Bob,

Thanks a lot. Listen Bob this job does not require your much time or space. It's lucrative but all we need is you handling and collecting payments from our clients.You do not need a uniform for this and get 10% of each payment. You can give yourself any title you want. Please give us your full personal and banking details so we can get started with this now Bob,

Thanks,
Xiong

From: Bob Servant
To: LANZHOU GLOBAL LTD
Subject: Thoughts on a uniform

Xiong,

Call me old-fashioned but if you are working then you wear a uniform, it's as simple as that. I can arrange my own uniform, what kind of look do you go for yourself?
With regards to the information you need, can you please be a bit more specific. Your new employee, a proud member of the Lanzhou Team,

The Big Man,
Bob Servant

From: LANZHOU GLOBAL LTD
To: Bob Servant
Subject: APPLICATION FORM

Hello Big Man!

We are glad to have you as our staff, this is the information that we need. Do what you think is best for a uniform Bob. We trust you. I wear a suit.

PERSONAL DETAILS

First Name:
Middle Name:
Last Name:
Date Of Birth:
Sex:
Occupation:
Marital Status:
National Insurance Number/Social Security Number:
Address:
City:
State:
Zip/Postal Code:
Country:
Home Phone:
Mobile Phone:
Fax:

CERTIFICATION:

I hereby certify that all entries are true and complete. I agree and understand that any falsification of information, regardless of time of discovery, may cause forfeiture on my part of employment in the service of Lanzhou Global Manufacturing Co. Ltd. I consent to criminal history background checks.

Date:

Applicant Signature:
OFFICIAL USE ONLY:
Remarks:

Lanzhou Global Manufacturing Co., Ltd.
■■■■■■■■■■■■■
■■■■■■■■■■■■■
■■■■■■■■■■■■■■■■■■
Thailand.

_____

From: Bob Servant
To: LANZHOU GLOBAL LTD Subject: UNIFORMS

Xiong,

I think I have it - a boilersuit that I bought for £30 from Nipper Kolacz, who works at the Michelin. Here's what I want to do with it. On the front left chest pocket I want to put my initials – BGS – like what football managers have on their training jackets. On the back I was thinking we could have the following slogan, which is fun and 'grabby'.

ARE YOU LAUGHING AT OUR RUBBER? SHUT UP OR WE'LL BELT YOU!
LANZHOU GLOBAL - THE BEST RUBBER BELTS IN THE WORLD BAR NONE

What do you think? It's extremely funny but also presents us as a serious international rubber belt company.

One final thing, are we going to advertise the fact that we have touched down in Scotland?

Bob Servant, star man of Lanzhou Global Ltd, clocking off!

Yours,
Barbara

From: LANZHOU GLOBAL LTD
To: Bob Servant
Subject: Form needed

Dear Bob (what is Barbara),

I am glad to read your message, I am very impressed with you and I must say you might be one of our best staff because of your good attitude and loyalty. I am proud of you and I feel you can help us have a large market in the UK. The uniform sounds perfect. You should wear it when you are doing your business as you will look smart. Let us have a think about what advertisements we might do but you have made a good start. Bob, do not hesitate to send back your job application form. It is very important and we need this information for our system. We also have clients that will start making payments into your banking account very soon,

XIONG

From: Bob Servant
To: LANZHOU GLOBAL LTD
Subject: Completed Form (stick it in your pipe and smoke it!) (only joking) (though you can if you want) (don't choke to death without paying me though!) (only joking)

Xiong,
Form attached,

Bob

JOB APPLICATION FORM PERSONAL DETAILS

First Name: BOB
Middle Name: GODZILLA
Last Name: SERVANT
Date Of Birth: 64 YEARS OLD DO NOT CELEBRATE BIRTHDAY BECAUSE
OF STRESS OF ORGANISING PARTY
Sex: MALE (CAN PROVIDE EVIDENCE)
Occupation: SCOTTISH REPRESENTATIVE FOR LANZHOU GLOBAL LTD
Marital Status: SINGLE/AVAILABLE
National Insurance Number/Social Security Number: WOULD RATHER
WORK CASH IN HAND PLEASE
Address: 18 HARBOUR VIEW City: DUNDEE State: TAYSIDE Zip/Postal
Code: ZIP? Country: SCOTLAND
Home Phone: BROKEN
Mobile Phone: YES
Fax: NO
FOR OFFICIAL USE ONLY:
Remarks: BOB IS A GOOD GUY

From: LANZHOU GLOBAL LTD
To: Bob Servant
Subject : MISSING INFORMATION

Hello Bob,

Thank you for sending the form but it is not totally correct. You did not give us your postal address and no national insurance number. Kindly do that and meanwhile one of our clients is ready to make a payment so we need your phone number and bank details soon,

Thank You,
XIONG

From: Bob Servant
To: LANZHOU GLOBAL LTD
Subject: STAFF PARTY

Xiong,

I know you want to get these forms done but it's not all about paperwork in business Xiong, as you know. We need to get the word out that there is a new player in the rubber belt game.

I've started spreading the word locally in Broughty Ferry, and people are intrigued and fascinated by what we are doing. I have also been thinking about a staff night out. Obviously, as things stand there is just me here in the Scottish office, but I was thinking of inviting a couple of people. The first guy I thought of was Clive, the manager at the Royal Bank. The other one is Hamish McAlpine, the former Dundee United goalkeeper. Hamish is a distinctive local character and a good guy to have onside. I have attached a photo.

With regards to locations, then I think that Chinese would be the most appropriate as I'm sure you agree! Shall I just keep a receipt and send it over to you?

Anyway, I'd better be off. I've got a major marketing plan for the next few days, which I will tell you about later. I'm hoping to surprise you with some great news.

Your Faithful Employee and (I hope) Friend,
Bob Servant

From: LANZHOU GLOBAL LTD
To: Bob Servant
Subject: Information Bob

Bob,

Thank you again for your hard work for the company. I think that the party is a good idea and yes we would prefer you to eat at a Chinese restaurant as we are a Chinese company originally. But Bob you have still not given us your national insurance number, bank account information and phone number right away. Also, we cannot find a record of your address, have you written it properly? Please hurry

Bob
Xiong

From: Bob Servant
To: LANZHOU GLOBAL LTD
Subject: Will the rain affect the belts?

Xiong,

My address is 18 Harbour View, Broughty Ferry.

I do have a National Insurance number, it is ■■■■■■■■■. However, I would really not want to get the Government involved. I have not paid any taxes since '89 and that was by mistake. Unfortunately I do not have a phone right now. I could source one though. There's a nice one in the Argos Catalogue for £8.99 but my Argos Catalogue is three years old so you can probably stick a pound or two on top of that.

Things have been going really well with getting people talking about the business. One thing though, a lot of people are excited but ask me the same question - What do the rubber belts look like and how much are they going to cost? There is some resistance from the usual suspects. Tommy Peanuts said that rubber belts would shrink in the rain and cut off the circulation to your legs.

The staff party is booked for Willy's Chinese Palace. Chick Devine, the barman at Stewpot's, is making up the four. I went to the bank and confirmed with Clive as well. He went all weird, bright red and saying how excited he was,

Your best worker,

Bob Servant

From: LANZHOU GLOBAL LTD
To: Bob Servant
Subject: Thank you Bob

Bob,

How are you? Thank you for the information. We are now going to set up the first payment to you of £3,000. You can take £300 commission from this as reward for all your hard work. You can also take the money for the party at Willy's Palace. We would like you to have a good time at the party so will pay what you need in extra commission.

So now Bob we just need your bank information. Please send this so I can have everything set up,

Thanks you and well done,
Xiong

From: Bob Servant
To: LANZHOU GLOBAL LTD
Subject: PARTY TIME FOR LANZHOU!

Xiong,

Well, this is it, the day of the LANZHOU GLOBAL LIMITED (SCOTLAND) staff night out.

I popped my head through the door at Stewpot's and shouted over to Chick Devine if Hamish was definitely going to be there. He said "Yeah, that's right Bob, Hamish McAlpine's going to your party" and everyone laughed, but that's because they're jealous.

Listen, Xiong, I am going to speak to Clive at the party about the banking needs for LANZHOU GLOBAL. What kind of account do I need? I'm not bothered, as long as I get one of those plastic card holders. Tommy Peanuts has one and he's forever flashing it about. The way he lets the thing fall open at the bar you'd think he was from the fucking FBI.

Your faithful employee and one of your best friends,
Bob

From: LANZHOU GLOBAL LTD
To: Bob Servant
Subject: RE: PARTY TIME FOR LANZHOU!

Hello BOB,

We are a little concerned as we checked your name and address on the UK directory online but we could not find it. So how do we know you are whom you claim to be? Also this is no joke, this is a job offer and we want you to take it serious. We have clients who want to make payment with cheque and balance transfer but we are afraid that it seems the details you gave is incorrect and you are not taking us serious.

We hope you are not a joke Bob. Kindly mail back.

XIONG

From: Bob Servant
To: LANZHOU GLOBAL LTD
Subject: Party, Address
Xiong,

Total nightmare. Hamish was a no-show, Chick Devine is full of shit, and Clive thought we were on a romantic excursion (?). See the attached. Yours in shame,

Bob

Dundee Evening Telegraph
Broughty Ferry News   28·03·07

Filed 01.04.07 by Broughty Ferry Breaking News Team

CHINESE COMPANY'S CHRISTMAS NIGHT OUT ENDS IN FARCICAL SCENES

Chaos reigned at a Broughty Ferry restaurant last night when two local men celebrated a Christmas night out that ended with one of them tying the other to a postbox and force-feeding him prawn crackers. The victim, who was dressed in women's clothing and has asked not to be named, required medical treatment at the scene by paramedics in what police described today as 'a moment of madness' from the attacker, Robert Servant (62) of Harbour View Road.

The night, sponsored by Chinese company Lanzhou Global Development Ltd, for whom Mr Servant is Director of Operations (Scotland), got off to a bizarre beginning according to witnesses. When Mr Servant arrived at Willy's Chinese Palace restaurant in Gray Street, he was 'astonished' to see his fellow diner sitting waiting for him, according to manager Willy Yuan.

'Mr Servant, who we have had trouble with before, went berserk,' said Mr Yuan this morning. 'He started shouting, "What the hell's up with your get up? Why are you wearing a f**king dress?" And then he was saying, "Where's Hamish? Where's Hamish?" It was very frightening indeed and it was a relief when he finally sat down.'

The staff say they were too

scared to tackle Mr Servant who then proceeded to dine in silence with his companion, a situation that seemingly ended when Mr Servant felt he had been cheated out of his share of the communal bowl of prawn crackers.

'That was when things got completely out of hand,' said Mr Yuan. 'The two of them started shouting and fighting and it spilled out onto the street. Mr Servant seemed to have a number of men's belts with him and he used these to tie his friend to the postbox. Then he ran back in and stole some bags of prawn crackers and went back outside.

'We locked the doors but we could see him stuffing the crackers into his friend's mouth and that was when we called the police. He was shouting, "Happy now? Happy now?" It was terrifying. I told the waiter to close the curtains and we didn't open them until we heard the sirens.'

Mr Servant was arrested at the scene but later released when the victim of the attack refused to press charges. A police spokesman today confirmed that Mr Servant was known to them and his future behaviour would be observed. Mr Servant was not available for comment and his house showed little signs of life while Lanzhou Global Development Ltd could not be traced at the time of going to press.

From: LANZHOU GLOBAL LTD

To: Bob Servant
Subject: I am sorry Bob

Hello Bob,

Do not worry about the party. Sometimes when men are together things happen that no-one is proud of. The newspaper will forget about it I am sure as have the police. That is more important as you cannot work for us in jail!

A client wants to make payment with balance transfer. You know what this is? So he needs your credit card long number and the limit so he can make the payment on it. Also can I know which bank you use? I know there is now a problem with Clive so let me know what bank you will use.

Thanks
Xiong

From: Bob Servant
To: LANZHOU GLOBAL LTD
Subject: IT'S OVER

Xiong,

My friend. I hope that you can see my reasons for saying what I am about to say. We've had some good times and worked extremely hard to get LANZHOU GLOBAL LTD the respect that it undoubtedly deserves. But nothing lasts forever.

Xiong, I'm holding up my hands and taking on the long walk. I know what you might think, that old Bob here has lost his bottle. That ten years ago Bob Servant would have turned round to the critics of LANZHOU GLOBAL LTD and told them to shut it, that we were going to show them we meant business and that, come the summer, every man and his dog in Dundee would be wearing one of our rubber belts. And you know what, Xiong, maybe you'd be right.

It's the paper Xiong. They just kept on my bloody back, coming round and ringing the bell and shouting 'come on Mr Servant, we only want a quick word'. But they didn't just want a quick word Xiong. They wanted their pound of flesh and, this afternoon, I suppose that's just what they got.

I summoned them for a clear the air chat and things went "not too bad". I attach the article below.

I suppose this is goodbye Xiong. I can't believe I'm writing these words.

God Bless Xiong and God Bless LANZHOU GLOBAL LTD.

Your ex-employee but lifelong friend.

Bob 'Xiong' Servant

Dundee Evening Telegraph
Broughty Ferry News   30·03·07

Filed 03.04.07 by Broughty Ferry Breaking News Follow-up Squad

BROUGHTY FERRY MAN CUTS TIES WITH CHINESE FIRM

A Broughty Ferry man who recently sparked havoc in a local restaurant has announced that he is cutting all ties with the Chinese firm that sponsored the evening and had been rumoured to be considering a major financial investment in the Dundee area.

Robert Servant (62) say that, though he has had 'the time of his life' since taking a senior position with the company, Lanzhou Global Ltd, he feels it 'is in the best interests of everyone' that they go their separate ways.

'I was approached by Lanzhou a couple of weeks ago now,' said Mr Servant this afternoon during an impromptu press conference in the beer garden of The Fishermen's Public Bar, 'and they gave me a really terrific post. Basically, the company makes rubber belts and we hoped that we would see a lot of people in Dundee making the switch from leather to rubber and so on.

'It could have been a great thing for Dundee and it was exciting to be involved,' added Mr Servant, who is being unofficially represented by disgraced local lawyer Mike 'Pop' Wood. 'There was then a bit of a mix-up at the staff night out [Mr Servant was involved in an altercation that resulted in both the police and ambulance services being called to Willy's Chinese Palace in Gray Street] and I really think that it may have soiled the whole project.

'More to the point, it has come to my attention that rubber belts are not big sellers. Quite frankly, we did not get the interest that we would have hoped. I think, and I'm not just talking about rubber, people should not be so scared of trying new things. I think in ten years' time we'll all be wearing rubber belts, but that won't make me sad. In fact, it would make me happy because it would shut up the boo boys.'

From: LANZHOU GLOBAL LTD To: Bob Servant
Subject: Re: IT'S OVER

Hi How are you? I know from the start you are a clown, I laugh a lot when i read from you, you are such a joker.

From: Bob Servant
To: LANZHOU GLOBAL LTD
Subject: That's the spirit!

Hello there,

Good to hear from you. Yes, I was pulling your leg. I'm glad that you also enjoyed the whole thing. It's a hobby I suppose.

All the best with the 'Lanzhou' line. If you don't mind me saying so, I think it needs a little bit of polishing. Tell me, where are you from and do many people actually fall for this stuff?

Stay strong,
Bob Servant

From: LANZHOU GLOBAL LTD
To: Bob Servant
Subject: re: That's the spirit!

Hello Bob, Of course many people do fall for it, you know lots of gimimicks now and you make your cash. If you also have anything to tell me let me know. I am from Malaysia, tell me more about you.

NO REPLY

Hello Bob,
My husband recently made a joke at a party and got a mediocre
laugh and it's all gone to his head. He's not a funny man, Bob, but
he's carrying on like he's Billy Connolly. How do I get him to go easy
with the 'jokes'?
'We've Created a Monster', Lerwick, Shetland

* * * * *

Friend,
This happened with Frank in the nineties. He made a joke at Safeway
and a passing postman laughed. For a week Frank thought he was
Tommy Cooper until I discovered to my relief the postie had been
sectioned. You need to find a way to have everyone who laughed at
your husband's joke sectioned. It may cause them minor
inconvenience but if it makes your husband give up the gags then it's
more than worth it.
Yours,
Bob

Dear Bob,

Our son is falling in with a rough crowd. I'm a bag of nerves and his
dad's hopeless, as always. What can we do?

Brenda D, Bolton

* * * * *

Brenda,

Your son is quite rightly seeking the exciting, edgy atmosphere that you
and your husband are clearly failing to provide at home. One obvious
path would be to give your house a 'jailhouse' atmosphere. Put up
posters of near-naked women, and give each other risqué prison
nicknames such as 'Skull Crusher' and, dare I say, 'Brenda Boob
Muncher'. Your delighted son will soon realise he doesn't have to leave
home to find the gritty behaviour he craves.

Yours in hope,
Bob

Dear Bob,

It's not easy being a Brit marooned in France. For example, why is it the French make top-of-the-range bread, but when it comes to marmalade they are total rubbish? All my French pals ask me to get jars of Dundee marmalade when I pop back to the UK. Do you travel yourself, Bob? I expect the marmalade fiasco is the type of thing that persuades you to stay in Blighty.

Barry Fantoni, Calais

* * * * *

Baz,

You're spot on. I've got no time for the foreign-holiday mob. They come back to Scotland drinking Lilt and making out they're Christopher Columbus because they went to Magaluf for ten days. Frank and I are eyeing up a long weekend at the static caravan in Pitlochry but I'm in two minds. Last time we went Frank was a nightmare, moaning about how the milk tastes different and the locals look like they'd ogle his wife if he had one. We'll probably just go for the day.

Yours in hope,
Bob

Dear Bob,

Is love real?

Mark Bonnar

* * * * *

Mark,

Absolutely, look no further than my torrid history on the subject,

Bob

My "Love Strikes"
- -

1960. Mrs Harrison, Biology. It would never have
worked.

1968. A girl on the bus to Fintry.

1978. Safeways, boxed cereal section. A woman with red
hair. We spoke for a few minutes until she "had to
go".

1989-95. Anneka Rice. When Anneka was up in her
chopper on Challenge Anneka, or sexily persuading a
local joiner to put up a cupboard for free, I'd be
left panting like a hot dog. Once, when she was about
to do a swimming challenge in a bikini, I voluntarily
knocked myself out to protect my mental health.

1999. Safeways, spring roll section. It was the
nineties, 'Britpop' was in its ascendency and I was
standing in the spring roll section with my tongue
hanging somewhere near my knees. The reason? A heavily
made-up woman in a bobble hat. She had just swaggered
past me and left in her wake the sweet smell of sweet-
smelling perfume. I followed her to the condiments
section where she turned to me and said, "Do they have
any HP Sauce or is it just this own brand shite?" I
swallowed, my voice was as weak as my knees. "Own
brand," I whispered. "Fuck that" she said and walked
out, kicking over a bin as she went (she was heavily
inebriated). It took me four years to get her out of
my head. She was my "own brand".

2001. Dundee Swimming Baths. Two sisters I met in the
queue for the Whip waterslide. Just as I set off on
the Whip one of them said "Enjoy the ride". I went
down that yellow tube with my mind racing. Was she

just a fan of the Whip? Or was she being flirtatious, the
way that women always are at council swimming baths? Or
had I misheard her? The Whip's acoustics were
notoriously bad. Had she said, dare I say it, "I love
you"? Did she, did she love me? I was only wearing my
second best swimming trunks after the first pair got
burnt to cinders in an indoor BBQ fiasco. These ones rode
up my thighs and pinched my stomach, giving the false
impression that I was seriously overweight. And yet this
woman didn't care. She'd taken one look at me, alone at
the swimming baths on a Tuesday afternoon and decided,
"I want him and I want him real bad." When I finally
entered the splash pool I was in floods of tears. It was,
without doubt, the longest four seconds of my life.

2021. Broughty Ferry Beach. I was lying on my back when
an angry woman loomed above me. "Can you keep it down
please?" she said. "I think I love you," I replied,
quick as a flash. "He's drunk" said the man who loomed
beside her. "Would it be hopelessly inappropriate to say
that I have fallen in love with you?" I asked with old-
school Hollywood chutzpah. "You're pathetic," said the
man. "I wasn't talking to you," I said to the man, "Or
you for that matter," I added, to their Alsation. I
closed my eyes and drifted into sleep, my dignity fully
intact.

– 10 –

The War at Home

From: Sergeant Gary Kaltwesser
To: Bob Servant
Subject: Official US Army

My name is Sergeant Gary Kaltwesser. I am a trusted operator in the US Army Marines and currently on deployment here in Afghanistan. I am from Illinios and have 19 years service. We are under constant attack here and I am able to get on only when things are not wild but I saw your profile and thought we could have a connection.

Please dear tell me of your life and I will tell you of yours.

Your Sergeant Gary

From: Bob Servant
To: Sergeant Gary Kaltwesser
Subject: Morning Sarge

Sergeant Gary,

Thanks so much for dropping me a wee line from the trenches. It's wonderful to hear from a military man, and great to hear that the Afghanistan gig is still going. I know that the Iraq roadshow had its boo boys, but I would hope Afghanistan has a late twist that answers your critics.
Keep your head down pal.

Your Servant,
Bob Servant

From: Sergeant Gary Kaltwesser
To: Bob Servant
Subject: Hello there

Hey There,

Thanks for taking the time to respond, makes me feel we've got a connection already. I will love to tell you more about me it's just that I don't always get to log on there to chat. You'll need to know that I'm serving the US Army Marines and currently on deployment here in Afghanistan. I am from Illinios and have served 19 active years with different infantry units.

I have been to a bunch of hot spots around the world and continue to do so today. I generally socialize outside of the military community since I'm single and my peers are pretty much all married with children. I am an avid athlete, having played most sports at one time or another – everything from Adventure racing to Wiffle ball! Someday I'll move home and be able to surf, paddle and dive like I love to do.

Write back soon dear,
Sergeant Gary Kaltwesser

From: Bob Servant
To: Sergeant Gary Kaltwesser
Subject: Hello there

Sergeant Gary,

What a life you've had, I get nervous driving through Dundee's troubled West Ferry estate[35] so I can only imagine what it's like there in Afghanistan.

Gary, I hope more than anything that one day you'll be paddling like you used to. And, if you'll have me, I'll be paddling right there beside you. Fully naked.

Bob

From: Sergeant Gary Kaltwesser
To: Bob Servant
Subject: This is what I want also

Bob,

Thank you and yes we will be together in this way. I want you to know am a man of one woman, I treat my woman with respect and care. Am a caring man, who show my woman what true love means, i work according to word of God. I'm a romantic man, I love going to the beach, listen to musics, love taking a walk, love going to the cinemas. I would describe myself as very caring a gentle and positive person.

---

[35] See *The Dundee Courier, 16 February 2006*: 'Council Berated For Poverty "Celebration"' ('Dundee City Council were forced to defend themselves last night after marking the West Ferry estate's inclusion in an EU document highlighting inner-city poverty with a drinks reception. "At the end of the day a European title is just that," said a council spokesman. "We've put Dundee in the spotlight and on the lips of the Brussels top dogs. If anything, we should be applauded."')

I had like to meet a woman who is caring and considerate, someone I can trust and who will trust me and will always be honest with me, someone who enjoys laughing at the silly things that happen in life. Someone who is willing to share the work to make our home a comfortable place. Someone who likes to live in a tidy house too, I do not like to have things very messy.

What do you seek in your ideal man?

Your Soldier Man
Sgt. Gary Kaltwesser

From: Bob Servant
To: Sergeant Gary Kaltwesser
Subject: My Ideal Man

Gary,

Great question. My ideal man would have a decent line in jokes, just under my ability would probably work best, and should always let me finish what I'm saying before having a wee crack at something himself. Also, I don't like when men sometimes use their wives and families as an easy excuse to get out of things like sleepovers and I can't bear the ones that clasp their hands behind their backs and sort of rock on their feet while they speak. It's a cheap way of gaining control over a conversation and I will not have it. Not on my watch.

Hope that helps,
Bob

From: Sergeant Gary Kaltwesser
To: Bob Servant
Subject: Hello Darling

Hi Hun,

How are you doing today? This is the man I am! it is like a dream that we have found each other. The woman I will end up with will love to spend time with me but also have her own life. We will share popcorn at an early matinee, search for treasures at local garage sales and touch, feel and squeeze the vegetables at a road side produce stand. She will be a perfect lady in public and our time behind closed doors will be natural and giving. She will be my life. I will be her 'rock'.

I will send her roses for no particular reason, with notes like 'Thank you for being in my life'. She will never doubt my feelings for her. She will become accustom to me mouthing the words 'I love you' across a crowded room. She will know how I feel about her. I will love, protect and guide her. I am looking for a lover, companion, friend and wife. Let the passion begin. i have butterflies running in my stomach now, i have never feel this way before.

Gary

From: Bob Servant
To: Sergeant Gary Kaltwesser
Subject: Release the butterflies Gary

Gary,

There seems to have been a bit of confusion. I am a 64-year-old man from Dundee's celebrated Broughty Ferry. I hope that information allows you to lie back, open your mouth and let the butterflies fly away unharmed.

Having said that I have no problem at all with squeezing the odd vegetable, mouthing stuff across crowded rooms and sending each other notes. However, if we were to do that then I'd rather we were mouthing 'Isn't this room crowded?' and the notes said 'Fancy playing snooker?'

I thought we were going to be friends and talk about Army stuff but there seems to have been a terrible mix-up.

Bob

From: Sergeant Gary Kaltwesser
To: Bob Servant
Subject: So Sorry

OMG . . . am so sorry about all this, i also met a woman online and i thought she was the one that has been mailing me. You said about naked and I thought that meant you were a women. Anyways it's okay we can always be friend. Tell me more about you my friend and yes what do you need to hear on life in the Army.

Gary

From: Bob Servant
To: Sergeant Gary Kaltwesser
Subject: Army

Gary,

Don't worry about getting it horribly wrong on the skirt front. My pals will probably write 'He got it horribly wrong on the skirt front' on my gravestone.

My Army questions are really just the ones you must get all the time: How big is your gun?
Have you ever killed anyone? Can you do a forward roll while running? What I mean by that is would you have to stop running and do the forward roll or could you go straight from running into the forward roll?

All the best,

Bob

From: Sergeant Gary Kaltwesser
To: Bob Servant
Subject: RE: Army

Hi Bob,

Yes I have a gun like all Marines. We have different guns for different situations. We don't just shoot anyhow or anybody but i have shot 4 bad men on their leg while trying to run off to explosive area and some passed away but they are all bad Muslim and corrupted people. Yes I think I could do run and roll as this is the kind of thing we train to do Bob.

I can't talk too great right now. We are short of troops and also we got trapped in the desert where mines were everywhere so we have to go back inside the Capital until the whole mines was taking out. It's seriously messy out here for now Bob. We also ran out of ammo until the rush team came in and help us out. It is just for the grace of God that kept us all alive.

Have been hearing about the situation in Libya, please my friend tell me some more.

Your good friend,
Gary

From: Bob Servant
To: Sergeant Gary Kaltwesser
Subject: Bad Times

Gary,

Good to hear from you and sorry to hear things are getting so hairy. I'm glad you can do the run and roll and I strongly suggest you use it the next time you're in a pickle. It's a move that catches people seriously off guard. I used it at Dundee train station a few weeks ago which was, to be fair, a mixed success.[36]

I'm having my own problems over here just now, Gary. Broughty Ferry Bowling Club are holding their elections and I've thrown my hat in the ring as Social Secretary. I should be an absolute shoo-in for the role but there's a guy Archie standing against me and he's got the ear of the committee. I'm trying to find out what's going on and will keep you posted.

Keep running pal,

Bob

PS No idea on Libya, the Dundee Courier aren't big on foreign news.[37] I do however know of the boy Gaddafi because of the famous rhyme -

> If you're going to a cafe
> Don't invite Gaddafi

---

[36] See The Dundee Courier, 29 March 2011: 'Station Management Slam "Kamikaze" Fare-dodger'.

[37] See The Dundee Courier, 18 June 1939, p. 27: 'Moustachioed German Invades "Poland"'.

From: Sergeant Gary Kaltwesser
To: Bob Servant
Subject: Hello

My Friend,

Thank you for telling me about your life. It sounds like this club of yours has people with closed minds. This is not what I believe. I believe in freedom and this was one of the reasons I took this path. Now here in Afghanistan I am just trying to make this job work for my country and the people. It is not easy. Lots of civilians are innocent but there is corrupt suicide bombers and others who would shoot me and my men first chance comes their way.

What is tough Bob is not having the right provisions. I have food and shelter but I can always do with just a little extra for things like cigarettes and maybe some candy and things like this. Do you think as a friend you could send some money maybe just a little? $500 would make my life so much easier here for times when we are not under direct attack.

Gary

From: Bob Servant
To: Sergeant Gary Kaltwesser
Subject: RE: Hello

Gary,

No problem at all, I will send you some cigarettes, a large bag of fun-sized Milky Ways and some spare military hardware in the form of an intimidating costume (photo attached). What's the best address for you in Afghanistan?

Bob

From: Sergeant Gary Kaltwesser
To: Bob Servant
Subject: Hi

My Friend,

Thank you so much for your kindness. I cannot accept packages because we are always on the move and no-one must know where I am so the money is best. Thank you for this Bob I will think of my Scotland friend Bob when I have my rest days and can relax properly with my cigarrates and candy.

Are you OK to send it today by Western Union?

True friend

Gary

From: Bob Servant
To: Sergeant Gary Kaltwesser
Subject: The Bowling Club

Gary,

It's all kicking off up the bowling club. I was up there earlier and the atmosphere could poison a shark. No-one is looking anyone in the eye and Archie is swaggering about the place like Eric Bristow on a stag do. I don't like this Gary, I don't like it all.

Will report back soon Gary. Over and out.

Bob

From: Sergeant Gary Kaltwesser
To: Bob Servant
Subject: Do not forget the money

Bob,

Sorry to hear this you should ask about and get the true situation that is my main advice.

Did you get my note about sending the money?

Gary

From: Bob Servant
To: Sergeant Gary Kaltwesser
Subject: The Bowling Club

Gary,

Well it's as we expected. Archie's apparently sown up the committee. They're having a meeting tomorrow night and it sounds like he's going to get rubber stamped through. This is unbelievable, Gary. I thought Britain was a democracy but apparently I was wrong. You were talking the other day about

Libya. Well if that boy Gaddafi is run out of Libya then he should get himself along to Broughty Ferry Bowling Club because that mob would probably make him captain. It used to be run by good lads like Bill Wood and Jimmy Walker and it's heartbreaking to see it like this.

I was thinking about heading back up there and hanging about outside the President's window. Could you give me some military advice please, Gary? A lot of the time in films you will see people using 'bugs'. Where can I get a bug and when I have hidden the bug how do I go about hearing the thing? Through a Walkman?

Or you could just teach me how to lip read?

Bob

From: Sergeant Gary Kaltwesser
To: Bob Servant
Subject: Yes I can help

Hello Bob

You are having luck because I have 5 years experience in this field. First let me say please this should be confidential what i mean by saying confidential is that it should be strictly private just between you and me only so as not to jeopardies my life and my job.

For tapping in with a bug this can be done easily. I can give you an arrangement to buy one and tell you how to go about this. The right bug can be heard for 50 meters all around. I will show you how to use this when you buy it. this would be best Bob for you to buy a bug through me because for reading lips well this is very hard. Of course I can teach you from my experience but it would take a long time and is different for every language.

Your friend
Gary

From: Bob Servant
To: Sergeant Gary Kaltwesser
Subject: Just Back

Gary,

The bowling club is shut today but I know the president will be in there getting everything set up for the election later. So me and Frank are going to head up and have it out with him. What I need from you Gary is interrogation tactics. I need to be able to get inside his head, how do I do that? And if he doesn't talk how can I make him? Frank was saying his nephew was telling him about something called 'waterboarding' that the Americans have been going nuts for. Anything in that?

Bob

From: Sergeant Gary Kaltwesser
To: Bob Servant
Subject: I know this

Bob

Waterboarding yeah this is something that we have to doo from time to time to get what we need from the bad guys we catch in the field. Its real easy Bob but best for now you send me the money before you go up to the club and then we can talk more. OK?

Gary

From: Bob Servant
To: Sergeant Gary Kaltwesser
Subject: SHOW TIME

GARY ON WAY TO BOWLING CLUB FRANK IS IN A TRACKSUIT AND I HAVE ALL THE STUFF FOR THE WATERBOARDING ROGER OVER AND OUT FOXTROT BE LUCKY

Sent from my BlackBerry® wireless device[38]

From: Sergeant Gary Kaltwesser
To: Bob Servant
Subject: Western Union

OK Bob but go to the Western Union on the way and send my money.

From: Bob Servant
To: Sergeant Gary Kaltwesser
Subject: GAME ON

HAVE STRIPPED PRESIDENT NAKED HE IS LYING ON THE FLOOR AND I AM ABOUT TO FIX THE HOSE TO HIS MOUTH

Sent from my BlackBerry® wireless device

From: Sergeant Gary Kaltwesser
To: Bob Servant
Subject: Do not do this

Wait BOB. This is not right. Stop what you are doing. Clean up this mess with the man and go

---

[38] Bob Servant owns no BlackBerry.

From: Bob Servant
To: Sergeant Gary Kaltwesser
Subject: RE: do not do this

HE'S FILLING UP LIKE A FUCKING BALLOON

Sent from my BlackBerry® wireless device

From: Sergeant Gary Kaltwesser
To: Bob Servant
Subject: Stop it

What The Hell is now going on?

From: Bob Servant
To: Sergeant Gary Kaltwesser
Subject: RE: Stop it

IT'S ALL GONE SHITCAKES GARY. I'M OFF

Sent from my BlackBerry® wireless device

From: Sergeant Gary Kaltwesser
To: Bob Servant
Subject: RE: Stop it

What is it?

From: Sergeant Gary Kaltwesser
To: Bob Servant
Subject: Speak to me Bob

Hello Bob,

I did not hear from you yesterday. Are you there? Hope all now OK with this club and you can go to a Western Union?

Waiting to hear

Gary

From: DI Lansbury
To: Sergeant Gary Kaltwesser
Subject: Your Assistance Required

Good Afternoon,

I am a Detective Inspector at Dundee Police Station and am investigating the murder of a local bowling club president. Right now, the case is still very unclear but it appears that he was inflated with water until the point of what the pathologist is calling 'disintegration'.

My prime suspect is a man called Robert Servant. He is pleading his innocence and says that at the time of the murder he was 'having a picnic with an Annie Lennox lookalike he met at a car wash, not a professional Annie Lennox lookalike, just someone who looks like her.

However, we have now accessed his computer and I see you are the last person he had contact with.

Can you please explain the exact nature of your relationship with Mr Servant?

Yours,
Detective Inspector Angela Lansbury
Dundee Police

NO REPLY

Good Morning Bob,

Our boy won't let me watch him play football, he says I get 'too angry' after I had a (well deserved) pop at the referee last week. He'll let his mum go but I've been red carded. How can I talk him round?

'Sinbinned', Norwich

* * * * *

Friend,

Simply attend the next game as your wife, wearing her clothes, a suitable wig and imitating her voice. Your son will admire your initiative and be pleased as punch to have you back on the touchlines cheering on him and his pals.

Yours,

Bob

Bob,

My son told me the other day that he wants to be Prime Minister. The problem is, Bob, he's a cracking kid and all that but he's really not the sharpest. Do I keep his Downing Street dream alive or try and snuff it out now? Should a parent encourage a kid's dreams when they're totally unrealistic?

'Worried Dad', Arundel

*****

Friend,

Let me tell you a story about my old schoolmate Sid McLardy, a good kid but not the brightest (sorry, Sid!). One day his dad asked Sid what he wanted to be when he grew up. Sid said he didn't know so his Dad took him out to the garden, pointed up at the moon, and told his wee boy about the moon landings, the Apollo missions and the footprints the astronauts left in the moon's dust. And he told Sid that some of those astronauts weren't the brightest at school either, but they worked and they worked and one day they flew into space. And do you know what Sid – who everyone had written off – do you know what he ended up doing? He's a plumber. And he's shit at it[39].

Yours,

Bob

---

[39] See Dundee Yellow Pages p.162: McLardy's Plumbers – 'We'll Certainly Have a Crack at it!'

Bob,
My wife has put me on a health kick. It's all salads and vegetables.
What's going on? I'm starving and confused.
'Ravenous', Cambridge

* * * * *

Friend,
There's no sugar coating (pun intended) this one. Your wife's having an
affair with a greengrocer. Apply for a divorce. Don't confront the
greengrocer, I know from bitter experience they are arrogant with a love
of innuendo and he'll have the vegetable props to hand to take full
advantage of the situation.
Yours in hope,
Bob

Dear Bob,

I am slightly concerned my hairline is starting to slip back. I looked online and there's various
potions and whatnot but I thought you might have a better solution?

'Hair Today Gone Tomorrow?', Earlsfield

* * * * *

Friend,

Reverse any hairline slippage by simply shaving off your eyebrows and then painting them
back on a little higher up your forehead. However, be careful not to leave too much of a gap
between your eyes and your new eyebrows, or you will look permanently surprised which
could lead to difficulties in social situations and be harmful at work, particularly if you're a
doctor and often have to open test results in front of nervous patients.
Yours in hope,

Bob

Bob,
It's hard being a woman with all the body shaming and whatnot. As
someone who's starting to get bit nervous about the beach can you tell
me what is the perfect diet? Does it even exist?
'Bikini Shy', Liverpool

* * * * *

Find enclosed the Bob Servant diet. Please send £8.99 by return of post.

Stayin' (staying) Alive
with the
Bob Servant Diet!

SUGAR — Sugar is an important part of your diet as it gives you that all important "zip" as you go about your day. The best types of sugar are toffee apples and Terry's Chocolate Oranges, which both count towards your "Five a Day".

POTATOES — Chips are the healthiest way to eat potatoes because you just pop 'em (them) in your mouth without a second thought. Mashed potatoes are a slightly infantile way to eat potatoes. Baked potatoes are fine but suggest you have a lot of time on your hands and you're less likely to be taken seriously by your peers.

FRUIT — Largely a waste of time.

CHINESE FOOD — The
healthiest
type of food
comes from the
exotic "Far
East" and the
traditional
food of the

Chinese people. Their "Seaweed"
starter is pure, 100% good stuff
(ever seen a fat fish?!), while prawn
crackers are healthy as hell (ever
seen a fat prawn?!).

VARIETY PACKS OF CEREAL —
Just good fun.

CHOCOLATE ECLAIRS —
Delicious and
as light as an
angel. Scoff them
down guilt-free
while watching

Escape to the Country and feel like
the "Lord of the Manor".

BOOZE — You shouldn't really drink
in the mornings unless you genuinely
feel that you deserve it. In the
evenings NHS guidelines are basically
"don't take the
piss". A simple
rule of thumb is,
can you get to your
bed without being
helped by more than
one person? If so,
you're "good to go".
Cheers!

– 11 –

Sad Time Publishing 2

From: Owen Bell
To: Bob Servant
Subject: Help me

Hello my Dearest,

Due to my critical condition right now i will not hesitate to make known to you all about me so please do not deter as i am going to expose a lot about myself and background here to you. I am residing in Beylane camp as a refugee and as a refugee here i don't have any right or privileged to any thing be it money or whatever because it is against the law of this country.

My name is Mr Owen Bell, am 24 years old. I am from Liberia in West Africa. Am the only child of my parents and am studying law in the university before my parents past away. And my hope and aim to becoming a successful lawyer, but now my parents are no more. they were killed by civil war going on in my country.

My late father Dr Patrick Bell, before his death deals and owned a company in Monrovia Liberia, Please listen to this and try to keep it to your self only. When my father was alive, he deposited some money in a bank and he used my name as next of kin. Now due to my refugee status and the law guiding this camp, i cannot make claims by myself, i need a partner preferably a foreigner who will stand on my behalf to the bank. I am helpless without you, i am having no account, no raw money at hand for it is my wish to further life abroad. Send to me Your Full names, address , occupation and telephone number:

Mr Owen Bell

From: Bob Servant
To: Owen Bell
Subject: Quick one

Owen,
Ever thought of writing a book?

Bob Servant
Managing Editor
Sad Times Publishing

From: Owen Bell
To: Bob Servant
Subject: What do you mean?

What is this about a book I am telling you about my troubles here in the camp so you must pay attention and read again the email. I need you to stand for me to the bank

---

From: Bob Servant
To: Owen Bell
Subject: Hereís the gist of it

Owen,

Apologies, let me tell you a little more. I am the managing editor of a British publisher called Sad Times Publishing. We print, as you'll have guessed, sad stories and in recent years we've had some of the biggest selling sad stories in England including -

My Head Is A Whirpool And I Can't Swim - The Troubled Mind of Vernon Kay
Sticks and Stones Broke My Bones - The Rise and Fall of Wolf from Gladiators
Dumped! How I Pulled Myself Together and Learnt To Love Again by Princess Anne

I think your story could fit very comfortably indeed into our catalogue. We pay generously for the right stories and I think you're sitting on a cracker (not in a saucy way).

Are you in?

Bob Servant
Managing Editor
Sad Times Publishing

From: Owen Bell
To: Bob Servant
Subject: My price

Dear Bob

OK I understand. Well my story would sell millions of books all through the world and there could be a movie and TV for sure so for you it is chance to be rich. my story would be worth $1m and this is true Bob if you work it out so this my start price and now we talk.

Owen

From: Bob Servant
To: Owen Bell
Subject: Absolute belter

Owen

A million dollars? Let me tell you something, pal. A couple of years back it was in the papers that Dawn French got a million quid for her autobiography. And that's Frenchy we're talking about, Owen, Frenchy. Now, Owen, you are many things. But you are not, and you never will be, Dawn French.

Have you ever seen the clip of her falling into a puddle on Vicar of Dibbley? I laughed so much I soiled myself, then sorted myself out, phoned Frank, told him about it, and soiled myself again.

Yours,
Bob

From: Owen Bell
To: Bob Servant
Subject: This is easy and not a book

Bob,

I have told you some of my story but not all and you would not have written me if you did not see the book this could be. I told you this is just my start price and now we talk so make me counter offer

This woman cannot be the first person to fall into puddle why is this funny i am not pretending to be anyone but i think you are pretending to be someone with this nonsense

---

From: Bob Servant
To: Owen Bell
Subject: Give Up

Owen,

I simply do not know how to make this any simpler. You are not Dawn French and you need to accept that.

Bob

From: Owen Bell
To: Bob Servant
Subject: RE: Give Up

I DO NOW WANT TO BE DAWN FENCH TODAY OR ANY DAY YOU ARE SO STUPID AND YOU TELL ME TO GIVE UP WELL IT IS TIME YOU GIVE UP

Alright Bob,

My friend has taken to wearing fake glasses on a night out because he thinks it makes him look intellectual. A couple of problems – the glasses are from Tesco, and the majority of our nights out are in Airdrie, where we already look like a pair of intellectuals due to us both managing to wear a pair of matching shoes.

Michael Wood, Airdrie

* * * * *

Michael,

This reminds me of my whole briefcase farrago in '87. When my Uncle 'Briefcase' McCloud died, there was only one thing I wanted from his estate – his fun-loving Toyota Celica. When his kids selfishly took that for themselves, I was left with his legendary briefcase. It wouldn't open but it didn't need to. It was the height of the eighties 'Yuppie' movement and by carrying around the briefcase I soon gained a reputation in Broughty Ferry as a man who was 'going places'.

Then, one night in Stewpot's Bar, I was chatting to some skirt who were almost literally eating out of my hand when I dropped the briefcase. It split open and revealed around 100 photos of my uncle in an excitable state. As you can imagine, Michael, it was very, very hard for me to explain the situation. Under the circumstances, I did relatively well. I told the skirt I was a 'cock doctor' and my uncle was one of my clients who had just sent over these photos for urgent examination. 'In fact,' I said, in a flash of genius, 'I should probably crack on with it now.' Sitting in the corner of a crowded pub carefully inspecting photos of your dead uncle's erect penis might be your idea of fun, Michael, but it certainly isn't mine. I hated every minute of those five hours, and the briefcase was bound for the bin.

Yours in hope,
Bob

Dear Bob,
My husband and I work different shifts so our marital relations
are limited to the weekends. But he's taken to fly fishing on
Saturdays and I'm feeling a wee bit neglected. You seem like a
man who could help with this delicate matter?
'Frustrated in Berwick'

* * * * *

Friend,
Marriage is all about compromise and you need to find middle
ground between the two pursuits. I suggest surprising your
husband on his return from fly fishing by dressing as a sexy Captain
Birdseye (lingerie, seafarer's jacket, beard). That will win his attention
then you can hit him with some top-drawer pillow talk such as
'Here's my catch of the day!' and something about baiting his hook,
or him baiting your hook, or the two of you baiting your individual
hooks then hooking each other etc.
Yours in hope,
Bob

Bob

My boyfriend's started working offshore. We like to think we have a healthy sex
life. How do we keep that going with him doing two weeks on, two weeks off?

'Home Alone', Gateshead

* * * * *

Friend,

You have to employ the magic of phone sex. In 1993 I replied to an advert for a
barely-used Hoover in the Dundee Courier small ads. It belonged to a woman
from Forfar who had a voice as smooth as butter. The Hoover had gone but I kept
calling her, and the next thing you know we had the most torrid session of phone
sex. I enjoyed it hugely, though the people waiting to use the phone box were
absolutely furious.

Yours in hope,
Bob

Dear Bob,

I have a hospital appointment next week which I'm a bit nervous
about. I never like going to those places, everyone takes things so
seriously. Can you offer me any comfort or advice?

Much appreciated,
Steven Godden, Fife

* * * * *

Steven,

I share your feelings about hospitals. They think they're the bees
knees and look down on the little guy. I tried to make some local
improvements to the situation but my admirable intentions were
cruelly rebuffed. My advice is just don't bother going in, you'll
probably be absolutely fine without their so-called help,

Yours in hope,
Bob

HOSPITAL BANS "PATIENT FROM HELL"

Broughty Ferry businessman Bob Servant has been permanently banned from Ninewells Hospital's Accident & Emergency department after what hospital management called 'a litany of transgressions'. According to the hospital, Servant has been a regular visitor to the ward ever since he had his foot treated following an incident with a cat.

'Zulu'

'After Mr Servant was successfully treated, he told us he liked the "whole vibe" of the hospital and began returning daily,' hospital management told the Courier. They allege various forms of unacceptable behaviour from Servant, including repeatedly accusing other patients of being 'at it' and 'pulling an insurance job',

attempting to 'heal' patients with 'motivational speeches that appeared to be monologues from the movie Zulu', and upsetting patients by offering unsolicited diagnoses.

'Adios'

According to the hospital, Mr Servant's diagnoses largely took the form of confident predictions of the need for amputation which often 'involved Mr Servant suggesting that patients "say adios" to one of their limbs'. Last night Mr Servant rejected the hospital's claims as 'ludicrous'.

– 12 –

Lions, Gold and Confusion

From: Jack Thompson
To: Bob Servant
Subject: Delete This At Your Peril

FROM HIS ROYAL HIGHNEST, JACK THOMPSON

Dear sir,

Permit me to inform you of my desire of going into business. I got your name and contact from the chamber of commerce and industry. I am JACK THOMPSON, the only son of late King Arawi of tribal land. My father was a very wealthy traditional ruler, poisoned to death by his rivals in the traditional tussle about royalties and related matters.

Before his death here in Togo he called me on his sick bed and told me of a trunk box containing $75m kept in a security company where i amin the city of Sokode. It was because of the wealth he was poisoned by his rivals. I now seek a foreign partner where I will transfer the proceeds for investment as you may advise. I am willing to offer you 20% of the sum as a compensation for your effort/ input and 5% for any expenses that may occur.

Anticipating to hear from you soon. Thanks and God bless

JACK THOMPSON

From: Bob Servant
To: Jack Thompson
Subject: Greetings

Good morning your Majesty,
I want 30%, and not a penny less,

Your Servant,
Bob Servant

From: Jack Thompson
To: Bob Servant
Subject: I will speak to the bank

Hello Bob,

See these percentages was arranged by the bank and not me. If you insist on getting 30% of the money i have to call the bank.

Pls send your

FULL NAME.
CONTACT PHONE NUMBER.
ACCOUNT NUMBER.
COUNTRY/STATE:
I will be expecting those details.thanks.

JACK THOMPSON.

From: Bob Servant
To: Jack Thompson
Subject: Good luck with the bank

Your Majesty,

Let me know what the bank says. Tomorrow's a bank holiday here, I don't know if you have the same ones? My full name is BOB GODZILLA SERVANT.

Yours,
Bob

From: Jack Thompson
To: Bob Servant
Subject: Hello

Hello Bob,

I went to my bank. If you are now requesting 30% we have to go back to the high court to change things. I and my family members has added some amount provided you are going to be serious and trustworthy. We have agreed to give you 25%. Pls that is all we can do.

We need your telephone number, country, state, city and account number before we can go further.

Jack Thompson

From: Bob Servant
To: Jack Thompson
Subject: Let's try the court

Good Morning Your Highness,

As a survivor of Dundee's Cheeseburger Wars, I have seen too many good vanners fall to intimidation by a Togo bank manager. Please cut out the middle man, stick on a suit, brush your hair into a style that feels right, go to the High Court with your head held high and request the 30%.

Bob

From: Jack Thompson
To: Bob Servant
Subject: YOUR URGENT RESPONSE NEEDED

Dear Mr Bob,

In order not to waste more time I have agreed the 30% and have notified the court. Yes I have a suit which I wear for business meetings and my hair is always the same. Within these few days, I have developed confidence in you and believe that you will be of great assistance in perfecting this transaction. We have to go ahead immediately. Please email me –

1. Your address
2. Private Telephone and Fax Numbers
3. Banking details to enable transfer of the money to you.

I await your immediate response,

Jack Thompson

From: Bob Servant
To: Jack Thompson
Subject: Hold Tight...

Your Highness,

I have been looking at the sums again, and I have decided that I want 40%.

And not a penny less.

Bob

From: Jack Thompson
To: Bob Servant
Subject: URGENT FROM MR JACK THOMPSON

Dear Bob,

Please let us PROCEDE. I am not greedy. I will offer you the 40% instead of delaying the transaction. I want it done, no matter how little it will change my life. Send your details now. I need to meet with the security company immediately,

I await an urgent response,

Jack

From: Bob Servant
To: Jack Thompson
Subject: Taxman

Jack,

I do not want the money in cash, as there is no way I could hide it. The taxman tried to turn me over back in '89 when I was riding high on the hog (literally) in the burger vans, and that mob always come back.

Can I have my share in diamonds, gold and lifesize silver figurines of The Krankies? I can shift it gradually through pawnshops in Lochee.

Bob

From: Jack Thompson
To: Bob Servant
Subject: URGENT

Hello Bob,

I received your mail and I guess I understand it mostly but not The Krankie. As for the diamond and gold, I have access to raw gold. You will get your share in cash and some quantity of gold. Look Bob you are wasting some time in forwarding your details that I need urgently.

Thanks,
Jack

From: Bob Servant
To: Jack Thompson
Subject: Animals?

Jackie,

I cannot take my share in cash, too dangerous. I could take it in diamonds, gold, or livestock (lions). My neighbour, Frank Theplank, has a private zoo. I just caught up with him in Maciocia's chip shop where he was waiting on a bag of fifty fritters for his monkeys. I told him a little bit about all this and he is willing to pay $80,000 for every lion I can get him,

Bob

From: Jack Thompson
To: Bob Servant
Subject: URGENT

Hello Bob,

I just got in contact with a friend of mine who sells raw gold and I can now pay you through live stock lion heads raw gold...quantity (4). So now you need not worry about the taxman coming again you can always keep them in your friend's private zoo as you said.

Now send me your full details of yourself.

Jack

From: Bob Servant
To: Jack Thompson
Subject: Lions

Hi Jackie,

Great to hear from you again. You can get hold of 4 lions? Are they male or female? I will speak to Frank who will undoubtedly be very excited. Where are these lions just now?

Bob

From: Jack Thompson
To: Bob Servant
Subject: URGENT DETAILS PLEASE

Hello Bob,

The gold lions are all male and i have arranged for them. But Bob can't you see you are dragging us backwards i have been asking you for your details for the past days now. Pls reply with the following:

Full Name
Home Address Phone/Fax Number Banking Details

I will be expecting the above information.

Thanks.

Jack not Jackie

From: Bob Servant
To: Jack Thompson
Subject: OK

Jackie,

OK, things are now progressing. My full name is, as you know,
Bob Godzilla Servant
68 Harbour View Road,
Broughty Ferry,
Dundee

There's not much traffic which is perfect, so as not to rattle the lions. Can you please send me a photo of the lions without delay? I need to see that you definitely have access to them, before I confirm things with that halfwit Frank.

Your friend, Bob

From: Jack Thompson
To: Bob Servant
Subject: Details

Hello Bob,

Hope fine. The informations you gave me not complete, you only gave me your full name and your address. I will need–

Country
State
City
Zip Code
Phone Number
Bank Account

Pls give me the above information then we can proceed. As for the lions, I have to take some photographs of them, so you have to give me some time.

Thanks,
Jack

From: Bob Servant
To: Jack Thompson
Subject: Here you go champ

Jackie,

Zip Code – DD5 123
City - Dundee
Country - Scotland

I'll get the bank info later. The Bank of Scotland in Broughty Ferry closes early on a Wednesday so the staff can go tenpin bowling.[40] Please get the

---

[40] The Bank of Scotland in Broughty Ferry does not close early on a Wednesday so the staff can go tenpin bowling. They do so on Thursdays.

photos of the lions to me as soon as you can. Are they currently in captivity, or will you actually be capturing them yourself? By Christ, I wish I were on that hunt with you my friend. Helping you. And, dare I say, holding you.

Yours Faithfully,

Bob G Servant

From: Jack Thompson
To: Bob Servant
Subject: Pictures of the raw lions

Hello Bob,

You didn't include phone number or bank account. I have made arrangement in transporting the 4 gold lions to you. I have put photos below. One costs $299,000 so 4 will cost over $1,196,000 then the rest will be in cash. These gold lions will be bought from a friend of mine's company. So give me your phone number for better communication and bank information.

Thanks,

Jack

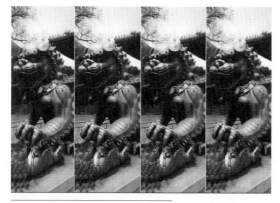

From: Bob Servant
To: Jack Thompson
Subject: Eh?

Jack,

There appears to have been a significant misunderstanding. I was expecting four live lions, not gold ones. If I stuck four lion statues in Frank's zoo then he would, quite rightly, think I'd lost the fucking plot. He'd tell everyone that I'd gone mental again like when I first got the cheeseburger van money through and wore a dinosaur poncho for four months. The four photos look great, if a little similar, but you seem to have got the wrong end of the wrong stick.

Bob

From: Jack Thompson
To: Bob Servant
Subject: URGENT

Hello Bob,

Hope fine. Sorry I misunderstood you, 4 live lions will be much easier for me. Look Bob, I went to that security company yesterday i was told to get $4000 to process the document for retrieval of the boxes that contains the money. I have raised $2000 so i need you to assist me in the rest of the money. Immediately you send the remaining $2000 and I will purchase the lions immediately. I will pay you back the money with percentages. This is urgent, reply immediately.

Jack

From: Bob Servant
To: Jack Thompson
Subject: Back on Track

Jack,

OK. Send me the photos of the live lions. Where are you getting them? $2,000 sounds fine, how much is that in pounds? The exchange rates in the Dundee *Evening Telegraph* are bollocks, they're done by the same guy that does the horoscopes.[41]

Bob

From: Jack Thompson
To: Bob Servant
Subject: HURRY BOB

Hello Bob,

Bob $2000 is £1700. Pls try to send it so I can collect the fund from the security company and send the lions to you. These is the lion's picture below. I have made arrangement of transporting it to you. I am buying four male lions from my friends private zoo and he has also arranged for shipment to Scotland. I will prefer you send the money through Western Union transfer.

Thanks,
Jack

---

[41] See The Dundee Courier, 2nd September 2023, "Your life will get better again, if you hand over a fiver for ninety seven Yen".

From: Bob Servant
To: Jack Thompson
Subject: LION PICTURE

Jack,

Greetings my dear, dear friend. Jackie, there seems to have been another misunderstanding. I looked at the website that is listed on the photo of the lion you sent and it belongs a Boston-based author and nature lover.

"I'm Tony Northrup. I live with my wife and cat in Woburn, Massachusetts, which is about 8 miles North-West of Boston", he states quite clearly on his site. Now Jack, I'm not sure if I can see the connection between yourself and Tony. Perhaps you sent the wrong photo?

Bob

From: Jack Thompson
To: Bob Servant
Subject: YOU MISUNDERSTAND

Hello Bob,

You are getting this all wrong. I didn't say that was the exact lion, I only gave you a clue on how the lion I will send looks like. If you want to see the exact lion I will send you must give me time. So Bob my friend you don't need to worry. This is Africa and you well know these animals are sufficient here. My brother even rears a cub that's a baby lioness in his house, so Bob expect the lion's photograph later today. You haven't said anything about the money I asked for? £1,700 should not take long to send?

Thanks,
Jack

From: Bob Servant
To: Jack Thompson
Subject: OK, I get it.

Hi Jack,

OK, that makes almost perfect sense. I look forward to seeing the photo of the actual lions. I just popped my head over the garden wall and had a word with Frank. He was busy cleaning out his Flamingo cage but he did say that he is very, very excited about getting hold of these lions. He has asked me to pass on a few questions –

Are they male or female? Are they in good physical condition? Do they talk?

I have booked in to see the bank manager tomorrow morning,

Bob

From: Jack Thompson
To: Bob Servant
Subject: URGENT

Hello Bob, Hope fine.

Answer to the questions.

1. The lions are all male lions and are very healthy.
2. I don't think I have ever seen a lion that talks.

I don't know if you are also interested in leopards cause my friend works in the Government Zoo and he could find a leopard for you? Remember to speak to your bank tomorrow.

Thanks,
Jack

From: Bob Servant
To: Jack Thompson
Subject: Leopards

I have spoken to Frank. He will take two leopards as long as they are friendly, and one elephant if you can get it? Frank is sure that he saw a talking lion on the television once. He thinks it was either on Songs of Praise or Bullseye. He says it reminded him of Jim McLean, the old Dundee United manager, in terms of its general vibe. Are you sure you can't get one?

I am going to the bank in two hours, I'm just watching an old episode of You've Been Framed to get in the zone,

Bob

From: Jack Thompson
To: Bob Servant
Subject: URGENT

Hello Bob,

Hope fine. I can get you two leopards. They are both not adults. I will try and see if the elephant will be possible and will see what I can do for the lion. When you are back from bank mail me and tell me when you are sending the money.

Thanks,
Jack.

From: Bob Servant
To: Jack Thompson
Subject: The Full List

Jack,

Frank will take the following –

4 lions, 2 leopards, 1 elephant, 1 alligator, 2 parrots, 1 hedgehog.

I said you might be able to get the two leopards and the elephant. How are you looking for the rest? And, of course, the talking lion? Frank has a good few quid. He's been my Acting Deputy Director of Sauces on the vans for decades, so he's got a fair bit tucked away.

Bob

From: Jack Thompson
To: Bob Servant
Subject: URGENT

Hello Bob.

From your mail I will only be able to get
4 lions
2 leopards
1 Alligator

The hedgehog, parrots and elephant will take me some time to find but I think I will first send the four lions and two leopards to you before we proceed with the rest. Bob please send the £1,700 now so I can send the 4 lions and 2 leopards to you. I think one of the lions may talk a little.

Thanks,
Jack.

From: Bob Servant
To: Jack Thompson
Subject: Sounds good

Hi Jack,

I will pass on the bad news to Frank on the hedgehog front. I'm not sure about a lion that only talks a little, I'd like one that isn't so shy if possible?

Bob

From: Jack Thompson
To: Bob Servant
Subject: THIS IS URGENT

Bob: This is urgent. What is hapening?? I don't sell animals. I only said I could get some lions to help you. Then you say you need a leopard and I say ok. Now you are saying the lion has to talk? What is this madness? Send me the £1700 that we agreed imeediately.

Jack

From: Bob Servant
To: Jack Thompson
Subject: Take it easy Jack

Jack,

What does the lion say when it talks? I am just checking that it won't get me into any fights.

Your Servant,
Bob Servant

From: Jack Thompson
To: Bob Servant
Subject: THIS IS URGENT

BOB LETS GO STRAIGHT TO THE POINT. THE LIONS AND LEOPARDS ARE HERE WITH ME AT THE BACK OF MY HOUSE THEY ARE FRIENDLY AND ONE OF THE LION TALKS. BOB SEND ME THE £1700 SO I CAN COLLECT THAT MONEY AND SHIP THEM TO YOU.

JACK

From: Bob Servant
To: Jack Thompson
Subject: Take it easy Jack

Jack,

I think your elbow caught the old Caps Lock there. Things are coming along nicely. I just need to know, for Frank's benefit more than anything –

What are the names of the lions? (he needs to know what to call them when introducing them to his Flamingos)

What does the lion say when it talks? (Who wants a lion that'll get them into scraps?!)

The bank is preparing me some forms,

Bob

From: Jack Thompson
To: Bob Servant
Subject: HERE IS THE INFORMATION

Hello Bob,

We have really wasted much time. Anyway, the information you asked for

1. The lion with more hair is Captain 2. The lion with black hair is Zoro

The other two do not have names, you can give them names yourself. I don't care any more. And as for the lion that talks it's ways of talking are strange. It does not pronounce words well it only makes sounds. Hope you understand now. Bob the security company has given me a day's grace. This is very serious, I don't think you realise what we are about to lose.

Jack

From: Bob Servant
To: Jack Thompson
Subject: All looking good...

Hello Jack,

Sorry about the delay. I was getting my hair done, I like to get a little body put in it for the weekend, but not enough to look arrogant. The bank need to know which account and country the money would be going to? I had genuinely productive discussions with Frank at Doc Ferry's bar this evening and he is absolutely delighted with the way things are going. He wants to know a last couple of things –

Can he call the other lions 'FANCY PANTS', and 'BRIAN'?

Do the leopards sing, and are they willing to wear clothes?

All the best babes,
Bob

From: Jack Thompson
To: Bob Servant
Subject: GO TO WESTERN UNION

Bob,

I am happy for your hair. Tell your bank to send the money through Western Union.
Name: ■■■■■■
Country: ■■■■■■
State/City: ■■■■■■
Branch: ■■■■■■

This is my very good friend name and address that is working in the bank. You will have to set a secret Question and Answer and be sure to send me the answer. As for the lions you can call them any name provided you shout when talking to them and always use the same name. And trained leopards like the one I have for you will wear any clothes you buy for them OK.
Jack

From: Bob Servant
To: Jack Thompson
Subject: Nearly back to 100%

Jack,

Things are bit lively on the van today, but I should be OK tomorrow to nip up to the bank. Just a quick question about the leopard, does it look a bit like this?

Good luck my friend,
Bob

From: Jack Thompson
To: Bob Servant
Subject: URGENT

HELLO BOB,

SINCE YOU SAID TODAY YOU WILL BE GOING TO THE BANK
PLEASE GO THERE RIGHT AWAY. AS FOR THE LEOPARD. THE SKIN
ARE ALIKE, THAT'S THE WAY IT LOOKS LIKE, SO PLEASE TRY AS
MUCH AS YOU CAN TO RECOVER SO YOU CAN BE ABLE TO GO TO
THE BANK. I WILL BE EXPECTING YOUR REPLY SOONEST.

THANKS.

JACK

From: Bob Servant
To: Jack Thompson
Subject: What a Let Down

Jack,

Bad news. I have just been to the bank and they said I can't send you any
money as I do not have any in my account. It turns out that I owe them over
eight grand. I tried to explain that I needed to send you this money for the
talking lions and the fully clothed leopard but the guy said I was, his words, a
"fucking lunatic" and got security to forcibly eject me.

I'm really sorry Jack, I hope I haven't wasted your time in any way, I can't
see how I could have, but I'm afraid that the deal is off. Good luck my friend,
and good luck with the animals. If they get too much then you'd probably be
OK just releasing them?

Love,
Bob

From: Jack Thompson
To: Bob Servant
Subject: Urgent

Hello Bob,

You see do you really still need lions and leopard? I will help you out sending it
for you free if you just send just $700 or $500 for shipping it to Scotland. Go to
another bank to send that money to me not this one where they don't respect you.

Jack

From: Jack Thompson
To: Bob Servant
Subject: Urgent

Bob?

Good morning Bob,

What is the most attractive you've ever looked?

Michael Kolacz, Monifieth

* * * * *

Michael,

It was 16 April 1978, or 'Golden Sunday'. I don't know what happened that day but I think about it a lot. I got out of bed and my hair looked 'just right'. I picked up a cardigan and the thing pretty much put itself on. My corduroys seemed to climb my legs like ivy. Then I hit the streets and it was like being at the centre of a skirt hurricane. I got home two days later with frenzied scratches all over my body, but with my dignity fully intact.

Yours in Relief,
Bob

Bob

As a recent divorcee my pals are telling me to get back in the saddle, but I've not chatted up a woman for over ten years. Any tips?

'Back In the Game', Glasgow

* * * * *

Friend,

My main tips would be don't start any sentences with 'as a recent divorcee' or use the phrase 'back in the saddle'. Other than that, just brush your hair and try not to break anything. That should see you hovering around a 100 per cent success rate, particularly in Glasgow.

Yours in hope,
Bob

Dear Bob,

Our local postie was an old duffer but he's been replaced with a young Adonis and it's been causing quite the stir. I'm a married woman, Bob, but my pal Jeanie is looking for the best way to approach him? She gets awfully nervous around the menfolk.

'All Aquiver', Dumfries

* * * * *

Friend,

The best way for your 'friend' to approach the new postie is through the use of double entendre. When faced by a woman skilfully employing a double entendre, every man in the world finds his knees weakening and his business end entering an involuntary spasm. It's one of the main reasons posties do their job. I suggest your friend opens with some 'special delivery' material and slowly steps it up to a level of (almost) unimaginable filth with various plays on her 'letterbox'. That should put her on the right path (pun intended).

Yours in hope,
Bob

Dear Bob,
I picked up a parking ticket because my new girlfriend spent twice as long as she said she would at the shops. Can I ask her to pay it and how do I go about doing so? I like her but I'm skint.
'Double Yellow', Edinburgh

* * * * *

Friend,

Suggest some erotic role-play where you play the part of a hunky traffic warden giving her a ticket and getting her to write a cheque, then simply pocket it. If she finds out that you cashed it then just say you did so for an 'added thrill'.

Yours in hope,
Bob

Bob

Man to man, is the first date the right time to ask a lass about her deceased husband's power tools? That's not a double entendre – he was a joiner.

Big John, Newcastle

* * * * *

John,

There are fairly strict rules for this and I'm happy to clarify. After a man dies these are the standard lengths of time for asking his wife for his gear. They are – his jokes (a week), his jackets (a month), his dog (three months), power tools (six months) and his ashes (a year, and even then some wives can be a bit 'clingy' on that one).

Yours in hope,

Bob

~~~~~~~~~~

Alright Bob?

Problems with the wife. She keeps trying to take me up town on a Saturday for some new gear. It's a nightmare. I'm a taxi driver with a generous build so shopping for clothes is a distressing experience.

Big Frankie, the Gorbals

* * * * *

Frankie,

A man's wardrobe is his castle. You need to tell your brandy-soaked (a hunch) wife to leave you to it. I wear leather jackets, the international uniform of the maverick, and set them off with a bunnet to show I'm a man of the people. With your build and line of work Frankie, I'd suggest a terry-towelling tracksuit. It's comfortable, it's warm, and more than anything it's a bit of fun.

Yours in hope,

Bob

~~~~~~~~~~

– 13 –

The Hunt For Jerren Jimjams

From: Dr. Mamadou Kouassi
To: Bob Servant
Subject: Opportunity

Dearest,

TRANSFER OF US$25m INTO A PERSONAL/COMPANY'S OFFSHORE ACCOUNT

We solicit your assistance. We have US$25m made from over inflated contracts in my Ministry (Federal Ministry of Education) here in Senegal. We seek your assistance to remit this amount into your account or any nominated account. Your commission will be 20% of the total sum, 10% for expenses and the remaining 70% for my colleagues and myself. Could you notify me of your acceptance to carry out this transaction along with your private Tel. And Fax number.

Yours faithfully,
Dr. Mamadou Kouassi

From: Bob Servant
To: Dr. Mamadou Kouassi
Subject: Opportunity

I cannot help you. I simply do not trust anyone from Senegal because the name of the country strays so close to seagull. I am sure you get this all the time, and I know it's not your fault, but I hope you can understand my reasons,

Bob

From: Dr. Mamadou Kouassi
To: Bob Servant
Subject: From Dr. M Kouassi

Dear Mr Bob Servant,

I receive your mail with thanks. Has maybe a Senegal man done you wrong before and that is the reason why you do not want this? I am not blaming you. Forward the hooligans name and contact information so that i can make an entry, yes i have the power. I forward to police headquarters to trace them and catch them red-handed. Whatever you lost you are going to gain it. Concerning my offer i don't know your opinion. Do you have details for a personal/ company or offshore account?
THANK YOU AND AWAITING YOUR REPLY.
Dr. Mamadou

From: Bob Servant
To: Dr Mamadou Kouassi
Subject: You got it

Marmalade,

You've understood me perfectly. The seagull was a red herring. The man from Senegal who ripped me off called himself –

JERREN JIMJAMS

I'm not sure if that is his real name. He said he had this secret bank account with $25m, I'd get 25%, and so on. The usual bollocks you get from that lot. I paid him over $50,000 and I never heard from him again. JERREN JIMJAMS is a liar and a fraud and I hate him,

Bob

PS Sorry I don't want to do the new deal after my experiences. I also don't have an offshore bank account. Chappy Williams has a cousin that works on the oil rigs so he may have one, I'll check.

From: Dr. Mamadou Kouassi
To: Bob Servant
Subject: Dr. M. Kouassi

Dear Mr Bob Servant,

Please my friend my name is Mamadou. I thank you for the information of the money. Believe me we will locate JERREN JIMJAMS since Dakar is a small place. The only thing you will do now is to send to me his phone and fax number so the operation begins at police headquarter. You give me the bank you were using at the time. I guarantee you we recover your money. They will vomit the money by force.

Thank you and remain bless.
Dr. Mamadou Kouassi.

From: Bob Servant
To: Dr Mamadou Kouassi
Subject: Vomit

Mamadou,

It would be great to see them vomit the money. Let me check my files for JIMJAMS phone number. He called from a mobile. There was loud music playing and I could hear a woman laughing. Also I remember JIMJAMS said he lived beside the sea and had long hair. That at least gives you something to go on in the meantime. Maybe I should speak to the police directly?

Bob

From: Dr. Mamadou Kouassi
To: Bob Servant
Subject: THE GENDARMERIE

Dear Mr Bob Servant,

These are useful tips. Now I have already laid the complaint and the Gendarmerie police assure me as long as you provide the contact of the criminal that he will be caught within days. As you describe JIMJAMS lives near sea and has long hair the order has been given to round up those who have this description. He said that you should contact him.

Email: Gendarmerie_office@yahoo.fr
Name: YOUSSOU BA (GENDARMERIE)

Please my friend i advice you send him an email and explain everything to him. Rest assured this GENDARMERIE is an action man.

Dr Mamadou Kouassi.

From: Bob Servant
To- Youssou Ba
Subject: For the Urgent Attention of Mr Youssou Ba

Dear Sir,

A good friend of mine, who I shall not name but if you think Marmalade you won't be far off, told me you can help me trap the notorious JERREN JIMJAMS who took me for over $50,000. I know that he has long hair and a female associate with a distinctive laugh. I would warn your men that JIMJAMS is a cruel and cunning thief. A man like him does not need weapons. His weapon is his mouth. Please beware.

Thank you,
Bob

From: Youssou Ba
To: Bob Servant
Subject: GENDARMERIE in charge

Atten: Mr Bob,

Well I recieved your mail with thanks and be pleased to hear we have launched a full hunt for the so-called JERREN JIMJAMS. You should not worry on how my boys apprehend him. In my country the people living near the sea is not populated and I will send my boys to the zone tomorrow. Everybody will present their ID and passport and anybody with the name JERREN JIMJAMS will suffer hell.

I will like to inform you that you will pay me £5,000 when i get him but you have to bear in mind that you will come down as soon as i get the robber so that we can recover all your money. You will pay me 1/2 the money immediately when I catch them and bring the rest with you.

I will like you to send to me your phone and fax number including your residential address.

MR YOUSSOU BA
GENDARMERIE INCHARGE.

From: Bob Servant
To: Youssou Ba
Subject: Progress

Youssou,

Your tactics for trapping JIMJAMS are spot on with one flaw. I am talking, of course, about the sea. Let's not leave the back door open. The land assault should be complemented by a simultaneous naval attack. It's up to you if you lead the land or naval charge. I would base the decision on whether you get seasick and what outfit you look best in.

I will happily pay a £5,000 reward when JIMJAMS is caught.

Stay safe,
Bob

From: Youssou Ba
To: Bob Servant
Subject: Send your phone and fax urgently

Attn: Bob Servant ,

I inform you that 9 men were apprehended and are waiting for interrogation. Send me your phone and fax immediately and prepare to send money through Western Union and also to come here to Dakar to collect the rest of your money.

Sincerely,
Mr Youssou Ba.

From: Bob Servant
To: Youssou Ba
Subject: Easy on the interrogation

Great news. Take it easy with the questioning. Get inside their heads Youssou, see what makes them tick. Where is the best place to fly to? I will have to really shake up my travelling wardrobe for this one. Any word from Dr Kouassi? I miss him a bit but not too much because you sound so like him.

Yours,
Bob

From: Youssou Ba
To: Bob Servant
Subject: Jimjams apprehended

Attn: Mr Bob Servant,

Dr Kouassi is just OK and happy because I have updated him with this. After the 9 men were treated like goats they confessed the truth. We found JIMJAMS office and the second boss of JIMJAMS told us where his mansion was. JIMJAMS was arrested at his mansion at 5am. He is in jail. He has agreed he took your money and that he took an American man's money as well. JIMJAMS has long hair and criminal eyes you were right about this. Now I want you to prepare yourself to come to Dakar and send £2,500 as we agree.

Mr Youssou Ba.
GENDARMERIE

From: Bob Servant
To: Youssou Ba
Subject: Incredible Scenes

Youssou,

You have him? JIMJAMS is captured? Thank Christ. Youssou, I need to see a photo of him in custody. I will send £5,000 reward when I know this is the case,
Bob

From: Youssou Ba
To: Bob Servant
Subject: Awaiting Urgently

Attn: Mr Bob Servant,

My dear here is the photo of Jimjams[42]. Now I need the money to settle my boys. You can send it by Western Union to these details.

MR YOUSSOU BA
SENEGAL - DAKAR
WEST AFRICA

From: Bob Servant
To: Youssou Ba
Subject: Oops!

Youssou,

My friend, you have sent a stock photo by mistake. I can't wait to see the proper photo of JIMJAMS in women's clothing.
All the very best,
Bob

---

[42] A photo was sent that was freely available online.

From: Youssou Ba
To: Bob Servant
Subject: Send money now

Dear Mr Bob Servant,

In fact it is a shameful thing that you are not trusting your friends that are fighting for you. Bob, forget about the photo. My bosses has ordered that nobody is allowed to see JIMJAMS until further notice. Please give me your flight schedule and send the money agreed for now today please.

Thank you.
Mr Youssou Ba.
GENDARMERIE

From: Bob Servant
To: Youssou Ba
Subject: Photo, Dinner rules

Youssou,

No problem. Just tell your bosses that I give permission or the gig's up. I am planning to travel at the end of the week and would like to take this opportunity to invite you and your team out to dinner. You can have starters and main course OR main course and dessert. Please let me know your thoughts on what courses the men would like.

Bob

From: Youssou Ba
To: Bob Servant
Subject: Assure me that you are coming

Attn: Mr Bob Servant,

I just received your mail now and I was wondering the type of insult that you are giving me? I used my power to have the so-called Jimjams arrested and detained just for your sake to recover your money. My dear the law of this country prohibits me to call a photographer to picture Jimjams in the cell, but you are telling me to picture him before you come and collect your money. If you want you can sleep in the cell with Jimjams if that is your cup of tea. My friend I will only detain this man for a few days until you send the £2,500. The American man has already paid and it looks he will get back every penny stolen from him by JIMJAMS.
We will have starters and then the main meal.

Thank you.
Mr Youssou Ba.
GENDARMERIE

From: Bob Servant
To: Youssou Ba
Subject: An American you say?

Youssou,

There's a Yank involved in this vipers nest? That reassures me greatly and I am willing to abandon the photo request. Could I please have this American's email address?

My flight is waiting to be confirmed. Many thanks for your offer to share a cell with JIMJAMS. However, I do not think this would be practical on a security level seeing as I will be a key witness in the court case against him.

Bob

From: Youssou Ba
To: Bob Servant
Subject: Assure me that you are coming

Attn: Mr Bob Servant,

Thank you for your mail and is well noted. Regarding the America man that Jimjams betrayed for $72,000USD.

Name : Randy Whyting

Email: gorWhyting@■■■■■■■■■■■■■

Thanks and awaiting for your arrival?

Mr Youssou Ba
Gendarmerie

From: Bob Servant
To: Randy Whyting
Subject: For the Attention of Mr. Randy Whyting

Randy,

How are you? You don't know me but I am a Scottish cheeseburger van titan named Bob Servant. We have a common purpose - JERREN JIMJAMS. I am sure that just saying that name has sent a shiver down your neck under your cowboy hat. Please, tell me what happened in your case?

Your Servant,
Bob Servant

From: Randy Whyting
To: Bob Servant
Subject: ATTENTION MR. BOB

Attention: Mr Bob Servant,

Well I received your mail but let me ask, who gave you my email? Anyway, I am Mr Randy Whyting from WESTBROOK USA and in fact it is a terrible thing. I trusted JIMJAMS in helping him by putting his money into my account and I will take 20%. He and his group collaborated with a bank of Africa to collect my $72,000 and disappear.

I promised the police if they capture him i pay $12,500. I have heard the man has been captured and so I am going to go immediately with the money that i promised. I am also going to Dakar for the rest of my money. If you are also a victim like this, I advise you to do similar, that is the truth.

Thanks
Mr Randy Whyting
WESTBROOK USA.

From: Bob Servant
To: Randy Whyting
Subject: Hello Randy

Hi Randy,

Thanks so much for getting in touch. You sound a little familiar, have we met before? I am deeply sorry you have also become a victim of JIMJAMS. Do you have an American landline I could call you on? Also, please send the photo of Jimjams. We should stay together in the hotel over there. We could curl up with a weepy?

Many thanks,
Bob

From: Randy Whyting
To: Bob Servant
Subject: ATTENTION MR BOB

Attn: Bob,

What up my man. I do not have the photo now as I deleted everything in my email but my lawyer in Dakar is a registered lawyer so he cannot tell me lies. My man I will be moving to Dakar as i told you. Concerning phone do not ask me about my phone because I do not know you before. Let us wait to meet in Dakar so we can see over each and get to know more better my man.

Bye

Mr Randy Whyting

From: Bob Servant
To: Randy Whyting
Subject: Good Old Randy

Hi Randy,

What up my man? I love the way that you Americans speak, it's so distinctive. When are you flying over there Randy? How are you going to get from the ranch to the airport? Any chance of a photo of you? Not in a saucy way.
Bob

From: Randy Whyting
To: Bob Servant
Subject: OK

Attn: Bob Servant,

How are you, my man? Please stop this bullshit about photo. Let us meet in Dakar and talk then. I am going there now and you should do the same if you do not want to lose your money. My friend all I know is that Jimjams is captured so let us go and get our money,

Bye
Randy

From: Bob Servant
To: Youssou Ba
Subject: FW: OK

Youssou,

Jesus, what's going on with Randy? Check out the email attached. The guy sounds like a loose cannon. I'm out,

Bob

From: Youssou Ba
To: Bob Servant
Subject: re:Randy

Dear Mr Bob,

My dear do not be upset by the American. I hear that he is a retired military man and his age now is 89 yrs ok so maybe he doesn't know what he is saying. I need you to tell me that you are coming to claim your money and you are going to send the Gendarmerie the money that you owe them through Western Union. I am totally disappointed with you just now,

Sincerely
Mr Youssou Ba
GENDARMERIE

From: Bob Servant
To: Randy Whyting
Subject: I have been a fool

Randy,

I think I owe you an apology. You should have said earlier that you were so old, Youssou just told me. Perhaps that's why your English isn't so good? I hope your journey goes well. I get there on Wednesday evening.
Many thanks,

Bob

From: Bob Servant
To: Youssou Ba
Subject: Back on track, clothing

Youssou,

All sorted with the 89-year-old real-life American Randy Whyting. I am going to go to the travel agent tomorrow and confirm my flights. I have been offered two travelling outfits. One by Tommy Peanuts who is suggesting I borrow his jogging outfit and one by Frank's nephew who played Dr Livingstone in his school play. Photos attached. Thoughts? Be honest! But not too honest!!! But do be honest.

Bob

From: Youssou Ba
To: Bob Servant
Subject: When do you come?

Dear Mr Bob Servant,

I think you should wear the blue outfit and this will be good as then you will stand out at the airport. You must send the £2,500 now or at the very least bring the £5,000 cash for the airport.

Sincerely
Mr Youssou Ba, GENDARMERIE

From: Bob Servant
To: Youssou Ba
Subject: A Special Request

Youssou,

I'd like to go on an off-road safari whilst there and wondered if you and your men would provide security? I am willing to pay $100 a day plus sandwiches. Please let me know if you accept, and what kind of sandwiches you require.

Bob

From: Youssou Ba
To: Bob Servant
Subject: I will arrange

Attn; Mr Bob

Kind to hear from you, I will be glad to receive you. For your security you
don't have any problem on the safari and also when not on the safari. We will
eat before we come to work also. So feel free as you will rejoice when you will
come down, confirm the flight name and number for me now. But you are
dribbling me like a kid, saying you will come today, tomorrow? Please send the
£2,500 in mean time?

Sincerely
Mr Youssou Ba , GENDARMERIE

From: Bob Servant
To: Dr. Youssou Ba
Subject: Why the long face?

Youssou,

I have confirmed the flight and need to leave right now. Chappy Williams is
taking me in his Sierra to Edinburgh Airport then I fly to Paris and then on to
your country. I will email you from Paris, Chappy's son is showing me how to
work his Blackberry so I will give it my best shot.[43] I am wearing the blue
travelling outfit as you requested. How will I know who you are at the airport
on Saturday? Maybe you could wear something similar?

Bob

From: Youssou Ba
To: Bob Servant
Subject: OK

Dear Mr Bob Servant ,

Good. I will try to match. Please remember the £5,000 cash.

Sincerely
Mr Youssou Ba
GENDARMERIE

---

[43] For me, this is the most outlandish note in the entire collection of Bob Servant's emails. He covers
his microwave with a blanket while it's operating and was told by Chappy Williams that he could only
make mobile phone calls from within public phoneboxes, a practice he maintained until early 2002.

From: Bob Servant
To: Dr. Mamadou Kouassi, Youssou Ba
Subject: FROM PARIS AIRPORT

Doctor Marmalade and Youssou,

Hola my friends and greetings from Paris on the Blackberry! See you both
at the airport I hope? Matching up to my travelling outfit is a nice touch.

My flight details are below, I cannot wait to arrive.
DEPART - HEATHROW - 1700
ARRIVE - PARIS - 2200
DEPART - PARIS - 0800
ARRIVE - DHAKA - 1730
FLIGHT NO AZ675436
BANGLADESHI AIRLINES
COST - $1764.45
See you tomorrow in Dhaka,

All the very best,
Bob
Sent from my BlackBerry® wireless device

From: Dr. Mamadou Kouassi
To: Bob Servant
Subject: OK

Dear Bob,

Thank you for the information and I will keep on waiting at the airport for your
arrival here in Dakar. It is Dakar not Dhaka. I am Mamadou.
Bye and God bless.

Dr.Mamadou.

From: Bob Servant
To: Dr. Mamadou Kouassi
Subject: FROM PARIS AIRPORT

Marmalade,

We're just boarding. A slight delay, the flight will now arrive in Dhaka at 1830.
I have changed my money into Takas and I will see you at the airpot in
Dhaka tonight. Ok, got to go. See you soon my friend. My love to Youssou
and Randy,

Bob
Sent from my BlackBerry® wireless device

From: Dr. Mamadou Kouassi
To: Bob Servant
Subject: Dakar

DEAR BOB,
THANK YOU BUT IT IS DAKAR FOR THE PLANE YOU ARE TO GET
THANK YOU.

From: Bob Servant
To: Dr. Mamadou Kouassi
Subject: You What?

Dr Marmalade,

We have landed to refuel in Turkey. What is Dakar? I am going to Dhaka, I thought that was where you lived? That's the plane moving again, I arrive in Dhaka in a few hours. Will you be there to meet me? How is Randy?

Bob
Sent from my BlackBerry® wireless device

From: Dr. Mamadou Kouassi
To: Bob Servant
Subject: What do you mean?

BOB

IT SEEMS YOU ARE JOKING WITH ME? HAVE I TOLD YOU OF DHAKA EVER? I TOLD YOU DAKAR CAPITAL OF SENEGAL WEST AFRICA. IN FACT I DON'T UNDERSTAND YOUR POINT? ENTER AIR FRANCE TO DAKAR OK. DO IT NOW BOB.

THANK YOU
DR. MAMADOU.

From: Bob Servant
To: Dr. Mamadou Kouassi
Subject: Eh?

How am I meant to change planes? We're at 40,000 feet. I'm not fucking James Bond.
Sent from my BlackBerry® wireless device

From: Dr. Mamadou Kouassi
To: Bob Servant
Subject: re: Eh?

ENTER AIR FRANCE TO DAKAR IMMEDIATELY

From: Bob Servant
To: Dr. Mamadou Kouassi
Subject: What have you done to me?

Marmalade,

I have just landed in Dhaka and, quite frankly, I am absolutely furious with you. Why the hell did you tell me that you lived in Dhaka if you wanted me to come to Senegal? I've wound up in Bangladesh. As if things can't get any worse, you and Youssou told me to wear this bloody outfit. It's absolutely fucking roasting here. I feel like my balls are on fire, the lycra is stuck fast and I'm losing the circulation to my legs. I have booked into a hotel and am going to stay overnight while I work out what to do next. Is there any way that you can get a flight over here and meet me? Christ, I wish I'd brought other clothes.

Bob

From: Dr. Mamadou Kouassi
To: Bob Servant
Subject: From Dr. Mamadou

Dear Bob,

Mamadou. I thank you for your mail. I myself is totally confused and I do not know what to do but the only advice I am giving is to board now from the Dhaka back to Paris France and stop at their international air port and then enter Air France or any flight that is coming to DAKAR CAPITAL OF SENEGAL in West Africa immediately without wasting time.

My friend do not be discouraged it is the mistake that you made because i always specify everything right from the begining till today, so more grease to your elbow, just keep on. I got information that Mr Randy arrived and the GENDARMERIE told me it now looks like JIMJAMS will pay up all the money he stole from you and the American Randy Whyting. I advice you start coming and keep me posted but concerning your clothes if they are now no good then we go directly to purchase new materials.

Awaiting your reply urgently.

By now.
Dr. Mamadou Kouassi.

From: Bob Servant
To: Dr. Mamadou Kouassi
Subject: Things are picking up

Marmalade,

How are you my friend? I am having a great time here in Dhaka. At first I wasn't too happy (as you probably noticed!) but I decided to give it a chance and I'm really glad I did. Last night I went to a bar and, well, I've kind of met someone. His name is KAZI and he works at the bar as a bouncer. His English is quite good and we got to chatting and I guess it just clicked. I don't want to get carried away, but I must admit that I do genuinely like him. The two of us are hiring a caravan tomorrow and he is taking me on a tour of his country. He wants to take me to his hometown and show me off. Imagine someone wanting to show off silly old Bob! Oh Doctor Marmalade, am I being a fool? Is there such a thing as love at first sight or is KAZI playing me for a bellend? Here is a photo of KAZI. I hope you like him. Be honest!

Bob

From: Dr. Mamadou Kouassi
To: Bob Servant
Subject: Are you coming or not?

Dear Bob,

Thank you for your mail and i will like to welcome you in my country here DAKAR IN SENEGAL WEST AFRICA but tell me when i will be expecting you? Or can you send just £500 now through Western Union and I will hold your money for you with no further charges? Your friend can come to DAKAR with you whoever the hell this man is.

Awaiting your reply.

Dr Mamadou.

From: Bob Servant
To: Dr. Mamadou Kouassi, Youssou Ba, Randy Whyting
Subject: Look out your party gear!

Bob and Kazi's Special Day
You're invited!
Host - Bob and Kazi
Location - Dhaka Church, Dhaka High Street, Dhaka
Time - Saturday, June 24, 12:00pm

Gentlemen of Senegal and America. Kazi, and I would like to invite you to our wedding here in Dhaka. If it was not for you, I would never have found myself here and would not have met Kazi. I hope that you can get time off from the hospital and the police station. It won't be the same without the three of you because you're such distinctive, completely separate characters. Please ask Randy if he can sing "Islands In The Stream" at the ceremony.

Kazi works in a travel agent and can get heavily discounted flights. Please send $100 immediately by Western Union and let me do the rest.

Yours,
Bob

NO REPLY

Bob,

Please settle an argument between my postie and me. How long should sex last?

Yours respectfully,
John Niven, Bucks

* * * * *

John,

An easy way to gauge it is to pop on an egg just before you start. Ideally you want to be looking at a hard-boiled situation but, as long as it's edible, you've done fine.

Yours in hope,
Bob

Bob,

What's the one thing a man needs in life more than any other?

Allan Reoch, Edinburgh

* * * * *

Allan,

I'd have to bow to my friend Tommy on this one. He's always said life can take everything from him, but as long as he has his 'peace of mind' then he'll be as right as rain. Although, now he's at the hostel, Tommy's also in the market for a personal safe.

Yours in hope,
Bob

Dear Bob
Where do you stand on public displays of affection? My husband is a
typical Scot and is not a fan,
'Wandering Hands', London

* * * * *

Friend,

With all respect, get your filthy mitts off him. Sadly, the downside of
having a pair of eyes that can twinkle on command is that women have
always been keen to fondle me. I've had to lay down fairly strict ground
rules. They can fondle me on the Claypotts roundabout in Broughty Ferry
during the morning rush hour (to show the rat-race commuter mob how
the other half live), in the bedroom (obviously) and in the condiments
section at Safeway (so I can make a 'looks like things are getting saucy'
joke to other shoppers). Other than that, I have a strict 'paws off' policy
and I support your husband in his brave stance. For the removal of doubt, I
attach a diagram of where men can be touched by their wives and others.

Yours in hope,
Bob

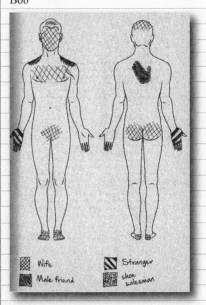

Bob,
My boyfriend hasn't proposed. It's been three years. I keep dropping little hints
but he doesn't seem to spot them. What do you think?
'Always the Bridesmaid', Glenrothes

* * * * *

Friend,
The best way to force his hand is to show him what a wonderful day your
wedding would be. When he's at work, create a vision of the wedding. When
your ring-shy husband comes back in the door and is met by the sight of you in
a wedding dress and your extended families gathered around, his worries about
your pushy nature will vanish into thin air and he will almost definitely propose
on the spot. It's a fun way of making him think about the situation, but without
putting him under any pressure whatsoever.
Yours in hope,
Bob

Bob,
As an ex-burger van operative myself, and one who knows about
oppression by the authorities, how did you go about dealing with
the local bureaucrats on the council, and specifically the
environmental health department? Do you keep it strictly legit in
your dealings with them?
Irvine Welsh, Edinburgh

* * * * *

Irvine,
It all comes down to the question, what is a bung? Is it a bung for an
Environmental Health Officer to visit the van every lunchtime, only
pay for a Kia-Ora, and get a triple decker meal deal with a fiver
hidden in the chips? Is it a bung for me to take him on an all-expenses
paid VIP trip to Zapzone and 'play dead' even when he misses me? Is
it a bung for me to satisfy his sexual fantasy (being prodded by Frank
with a big stick in a skip behind Safeways) and then to pay for Frank's
therapy sessions? The answer to all of the above, Irvine, is a
resounding no. I keep it legit.
Yours in hope,
Bob

* * * * *

Bob

Glad to hear you keep it clean. One question, would the skip experience be available to members of the public? I have a taxi to Broughty Ferry on standby.

Yours in Hope,
Irvine

* * * * *

Irvine,

Get in the taxi. Frank, sharpen the stick.

Bob

~~~~~~~~~~~~~~~

Dear Bob,

Which aisle of the supermarket is the best place to meet new friends?

Simon Tosh, Guatemala

* * * * *

Simon,

Great question. It really depends what you're looking for. Traditionally it's the vegetable aisle for romance (high availability of props for saucy suggestions) and anywhere near the fajita packs for that 'Anything can happen!' party vibe. What I cannot emphasise enough is do not look to make friends in the car park. I have formed various relationships of various natures in supermarket car parks over the years and it's always the same – they start absolutely superbly and quickly descend into the most horrible levels of bitterness and regret.

Yours in hope,

Bob

~~~~~~~~~~~~~~~

– 14 –

Bob's Phone Number

From: Christopher Michaels
To: Bob Servant
Subject: A proposal

Dear Sir/Madam,

My name is Barrister Michael Christopher, a Senior Advocate and legal consultant in practice here in the Cook Islands. My client suffered a terrible violent death life alongside with his wife in a Beirut-bound charter jet plane crashed on the Monday, 9th January 2006, 12:12 GMT (details on Internet if required).

Prior to his death my client secured a contract worth millions of US dollars from the kingdom of Bahrain. As his personal lawyer and close confidant, all my efforts to locate any of his relatives whom i can present as next of kin has proved abortive. Therefore I am seeking for your consent to present you as next of kin and subsequently the beneficiary of the fund. I will initiate this process towards a conclusion if you give me positive signals. I wait to hear from you.

Yours faithfully,
Mike Christopher

From: Bob Servant
To: Mike
Subject: You're at it!

Mike,

The Cook Islands? You must think I'm stupid. Where do you live, Frying Pan City?

Your Servant,
Bob Servant

From: Christopher Michaels
To: Bob Servant
Subject: The Cook islands

Dear Bob Servant,

What is this you are saying? The Cook Islands are recognised province. Do you want to act as next of kin? The commission is very kind.

Yours faithfully,
Mike Christopher

From: Bob Servant
To: Mike
Subject: I hold my hands up

Barrister Christopher,

I have just had a look at my atlas and would like to apologise, as the Native Americans say, 'with reservations'.[44] I accept that the Cook Islands exist but I am also nervous about meeting new people from the Internet. I am an elderly man and also have a good few quid (don't tell the wife!) (I don't have a wife) and this makes me a target for likely lads and chancers,

Yours,
Bob

From: Christopher Michaels
To: Bob Servant
Subject: A proposal

Dear Mr Servant,

Yes I understand your worries but do not worry in this case because I am a Barrister of course so this is legal and just. This is excellent Bob and I can confirm you are now the front runner to be the main beneficiary of this will minus our administration fees which as normal will have to be paid first. They are very low, only $200, OK?

Yours faithfully,
Mike Christopher

---

[44] This is one of Bob's favourite jokes but has always struck me as a little obtuse. I once probed him at a corner table in Broughty Ferry's Stewpot's Bar on how exactly this selection of words operate as a joke. He replied, 'A lot of people like Rolls Royces but do they know what's under the bonnet?' I answered that yes, those same people would be aware that under the bonnet of a Rolls Royce would be a Rolls Royce engine. Bob replied by asking if I thought the table had 'a wobble'. I replied that it didn't. Bob then spent five minutes frowning and wobbling the table with his hand before leaving for a lengthy bathroom visit.

From: Bob Servant
To: Mike
Subject: Phone

Barrister Christopher,
$200 is a drop in the bloody ocean. During Dundee's Cheeseburger Wars I'd earn that much by putting my shoes on and the same again for brushing my hair.
Listen, it might be quicker to talk over the phone. Would you mind calling me?
Yours,
Bob

From: Christopher Michaels
To: Bob Servant
Subject: I will call

Yes of course I will call you at my expense Bob just send the number

---

From: Bob Servant
To: Mike
Subject: Phone Number

OK are you ready?

From: Christopher Michaels
To: Bob Servant
Subject: Give me the number

Yes I am ready.

From: Bob Servant
To: Mike
Subject: Here we go

0

From: Christopher Michaels
To: Bob Servant
Subject: RE: Here we go

Hello Bob I think that did not come through please send it again.

From: Bob Servant
To: Mike
Subject: RE: Here we go

0

From: Christopher Michaels
To: Bob Servant
Subject: Not coming through

That did not come through again sorry Bob please send again.

From: Bob Servant
To: Mike
Subject: Seems fine my end

4

From: Christopher Michaels
To: Bob Servant
Subject: Not right

Bob this is not correct I am not getting the full number please check that you are sending it.

From: Bob Servant
To: Mike
Subject: RE: Not right

4

From: Christopher Michaels
To: Bob Servant
Subject: RE: Not right

Bob what is this? You are not sending your number properly I am only getting one number through a 0 and now 4s what is this?

From: Bob Servant
To: Mike
Subject: Eh?

I don't quite understand your problem, I'm sending it through. 0044 is the code for the UK. Next bit:

1

From: Christopher Michaels
To: Bob Servant
Subject: Send the whole number

What are you saying to me Bob? You're sending me the number one at every time? Why would you do this Bob just send the whole thing.

From: Bob Servant
To: Mike
Subject: Security

Mike,
As I told you I am worried about Internet security. Please give me the respect I deserve.

3

From: Christopher Michaels
To: Bob Servant
Subject: RE: Security

This is too stupid but OK. 004413 come on

From: Bob Servant
To: Mike
Subject: 8

From: Christopher Michaels
To: Bob Servant
Subject: Got it

0044138 OK more

From: Bob Servant
To: Mike
Subject: 2

From: Christopher Michaels
To: Bob Servant
Subject: More needed

00441382 more

From: Bob Servant
To: Mike
Subject: 2

From: Christopher Michaels
To: Bob Servant
Subject: send the rest now

004413822 more

From: Bob Servant
To: Mike
Subject: 2

From: Christopher Michaels
To: Bob Servant
Subject: RE: 2

0044138222 more

From: Bob Servant
To: Mike
Subject: Hang on

Sorry I've lost my thread a bit. I think I've gone a bit heavy on the 2s. Would you mind reading back what I've sent so far?

From: Christopher Michaels
To: Bob Servant
Subject: OK here

0044138222 send the rest.

From: Bob Servant
To: Mike
Subject: Remember the security!

Sorry, can you send it one number at a time? It's safer.

From: Christopher Michaels
To: Bob Servant
Subject: RE: Remember the security!

Are you serious?

From: Bob Servant
To: Mike
Subject: Good Question

What do you think? (be honest)

From: Christopher Michaels
To: Bob Servant
Subject: RE: Good Question

FUCK you if this is not true

From: Bob Servant
To: Mike
Subject: RE: Good Question

4

_____

NO REPLY

Dear Bob,

I'm a member of a popular beat combo and spend a lot of time on the road. I often think fondly about my childhood home of Fife. As someone who lives just over the river and probably spends a lot of time admiring Fife, what's been your favourite trip over the river?

Guy Berryman, Coldplay

* * * * *

Guy,

People say I'm always having a pop at Fifers, but the inarguable fact is that they are a vindictive and aggressive people. However, for balance, let me tell you about my favourite visit to Fife.

On a rainy day in 1993 I was tempted to drive to Fife to purchase a competitively priced clock radio. My van broke down on the Tay Bridge. I was inspecting it when a passing lorry driver threw a half-eaten sausage supper that hit me in the face. I then realised I was locked out the van. I stood waiting in the rain for the AA, during which time I contracted pneumonia, and another passing lorry driver threw a half-eaten mince roll that also hit me in the face. The van needed to be towed and I walked home to Broughty Ferry. While walking along the Dundee Road, a passing lorry driver threw a half-eaten lamb vindaloo that hit me in the face and caused temporary blindness to go with the pneumonia. I was in bed for a week. That was, without doubt, my favourite trip to Fife.

Yours in hope,

Bob

Greetings Bob,

You obviously have extensive experience in the burger industry, and it seems now with the introduction of the 'gourmet' burger, that market seems to be ever-expanding. Are you tempted to enter the gourmet burger world?

Greg McHugh, Hove

* * * * *

Greg,

I invented the gourmet burger world. I launched my first during the Falklands (the 'Belgrano') and ever since then have thrilled the punters with a conveyor belt of exotic concoctions and 'lifestyle packages' such as our popular 'Divorcee Special' (burger, chips, mug of gin, and small bottle of mascara).

Our bestselling burgers are the classic 'Widow Maker' and our newly launched 'Computer Burger', which, as part of our modernising drive, can be ordered on the World Wide Web. You just 'email' Frank's nephew Tyson saying when you'll be down, and he catches two buses to the harbour, jogs over to the van and lets us know. I attach my much-admired posters. Frank sometimes moans I put too much into the poster budget but it's worth every penny to keep us looking cutting-edge.

Yours in hope,

Bob

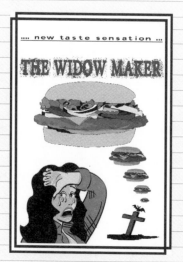

Dear Bob,

As a proud Dundonian who sadly got dragged away from the city with work, I often think back fondly to my younger years. And, in doing so, I remembered with some horror that we have met. It was 1959, at the Forte's ice cream parlour in Dura Street. You had a double cone (both sides were vanilla, showing a lack of imagination) that had dripped down your cardigan. I remember you were a curious looking wee boy, with a runny nose, and seemed to find it hard to communicate with women. Have things improved at all for you or, God forbid, got worse?

Brian Cox, Brooklyn, New York

* * * * *

Coxy,

You've got a bloody nerve. I remember that day well. You were clumsily chatting to some girls when I strolled over with one of my first and (arguably) best pieces of double entendre in a well-worked joke about flakes. The girls laughed so hard their eyes bulged up like marbles and a passer-by introduced himself as a top Hollywood showbiz manager and asked if I wanted to go to Hollywood with him 'right here, right now'. I said, 'No, my work in Dundee is a long way from being done.' He then turned to you and said, 'I suppose you'll do.' I walked away with my head held high, leaving the girls panting like dogs in my wake and your eyes brimming with jealous tears.

Yours in fury,
Bob

* * * * *

Bob,
We're both of a healthy age yet it would appear that your memory is starting to fail first. I was doing absolutely fine with the girls (in fact we were lining up a game of kiss-chasie round the Stobie Ponds for later that afternoon, and you know as well as I do that a game of kiss-chasie round the Stobie Ponds can be a far-from-innocent experience). You then interrupted and told your so-called 'joke' that failed on several fronts (logic, delivery, humour), leaving me to cause a diversion by bursting into song, which attracted the appreciative attention of the aforementioned Hollywood bigwig. You went up the road with your tail between your legs and I remember thinking that I would read about you one day in the Dundee Courier. I presumed you'd be arrested for an amateur-ish confidence trick or suchlike, so well done on surpassing my meagre expectations!
Brian

* * * * *

Coxy,

I think we're going to have to agree to disagree on this one, Coxy. The important thing, of course, is that we remain pals.

Bob

* * * * *

Bob

I think let's go for 'associates'.

Brian

* * * * *

Coxy,

Can I come and visit you in America?

Bob

* * * * *

Bob,

No.

Brian

Bob,

I am considerably younger than you, but nothing lasts forever. I wanted to ask what you think is the hardest thing about getting old?

Jonathan Watson, Glasgow

* * * * *

Johnny,

Probably, the hardest thing is the way my looks are maturing. I always hoped that my looks would mature badly, that in my later years I'd be able to shake off the skirt and concentrate on the bowling but I'm sad to say the reverse is happening. I'm aging superbly, the skirt is still being dragged along on my coattails (often literally) and my bowling remains highly unpredictable.

Yours in hope,

Bob

Bob,
You've attracted a fair number of misguided critics over the years –
great men always do, of course. What's the worst thing anyone's ever
said about you?
Peter and Judy E, Ockley

* * * * *

Dear Peter and Judy,

For 30 years I've been plagued by a woman from Fife who believes I
stole her walk. The idea I'd steal a walk from anyone is absurd. The
idea I'd steal it from a woman from Fife is the stuff of nightmares.

Yours in hope,
Bob

Bob,

You're an extraordinary man, and I don't necessarily mean that
positively. But you're also getting on. How are you handling the
ageing process?

Dominic Maciocia, Connecticut

* * * * *

Dominic,

Not great, to be honest. When I went to vote at the last election, I looked
round the voting station and thought 'Good God, these election officials
look like schoolchildren'. In fact, it turned out the election had been the
day before, they were schoolchildren, and I had to have a quick,
ultimately victorious chat with a Community Support Officer, but my
point is that I'm getting older and everyone else is getting younger. I tried
to stop the tides of time by joining the local gym, however, that sadly
turned out to be run by fascists,

Bob

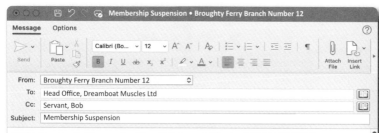

From: Broughty Ferry Branch Number 12

To: Head Office, Dreamboat Muscles Ltd

Cc: Servant, Bob

Subject: Membership Suspension

We have suspended the membership of Bob Servant, Member 8702345 OFF PEAK.

Reason for suspension: Continual transgression of gym rules

Detail:

3/6/15 - Mr Servant was observed loudly shouting out names while lifting a set of children's weights. This was distracting for other gym members. Names included Roger Moore, Adrian Chiles and Tony Hart. Mr Servant explained that while lifting weights he liked to think about people who have 'wronged him', for motivational reasons. Despite being asked to stop, Mr Servant continued to shout out names, including Princess Anne, Shabba Ranks and 'the janitor in Safeway who thinks he's in the CIA'.

5/6/15 - Mr Servant challenged another client to an arm wrestle. After swiftly losing the arm wrestle, Mr Servant said he had been 'talking to him' and pointed out an elderly gym member. After swiftly losing that arm wrestle, Mr Servant said he had been "talking to him" and pointed out a member of the gym's Toddler Turbo Class. After swiftly losing that arm wrestle, Mr Servant said the child was 'probably' possessed by the devil. This upset the other members of the Toddler Turbo Class. Mr Servant then attempted to 'exorcise' the child, which caused widespread panic amongst the rest of the Toddler Turbo Class.

8/6/15 - Mr Servant arrived at the gym inebriated. After struggling for half an hour with a single weight, Servant accused other gym members of having 'glued this fucker down'. He then approached other gym members and said they 'thought they were the bee's knees' and that they 'wouldn't last ten minutes in a war zone situation'. Mr Servant was later found sleeping in the disabled toilet.

9/6/15 - Mr Servant approached a gym member lying on a bench and accused him of having 'plastic' muscles 'Sellotaped' to his arms. He suggested that the member believed this made him look 'like James Bond' but in fact only succeeded in making him look 'like a bell-end'. When the gym member stood up to discuss the matter further, Mr Servant ran all the way to the male changing room shouting, 'He's got a blade, he's got a blade!'

11/6/15 - Mr Servant was observed popping his head into the female Body Pump class and shouting 'I wouldn't mind being an exercise cat!' Mr Servant then grew rapidly flustered and said he had meant to say that he wouldn't mind being 'an exercise mat'. Mr Servant was later found shouting at himself in the showers, berating himself for his mistake. This is not the first issue between Mr Servant and the Body Pump class, who Mr Servant refers to as 'my girls'. This has caused particular problems between Mr Servant and the male members of the Body Pump class.

13/6/15 - We received a complaint that while in the shower Mr Servant had reached over a dividing wall and attempted to shampoo the hair of another gym user. Mr Servant said he was 'just having a laugh' and that we should 'lighten up'.

17/6/15 - We told Mr Servant his membership was being withdrawn with immediate effect. Mr Servant said he was 'just about to tell us he was leaving anyway'. In the hour after Mr Servant's departure, we received several phone calls from a gentleman with a high-pitched voice saying that Mr Servant had just joined his gym and was 'the best customer he'd ever had' and had 'spent about eight grand on snacks'. The unidentified gentleman explained this new gym was owned by a 'professional catwalk model' who had 'taken quite the fancy' to Mr Servant and had asked him to move into her 'penthouse flat' which was located directly above the gym and connected to the gym by sliding down 'a brass pole like firemen have'. The unidentified voice – which had by now dropped several octaves – then made various double entendre about the brass pole, of rapidly decreasing logic.

– 15 –

Why Me? 2

From: Bob Servant
To: Rose
Subject: 'Why Me?'

Rose,

Hope all's well at your end. I've spoken to you a couple of times before about my book. Well, Rose, we've reached the end. The old horse has had one last run round the paddock and now we're all on the bus to the glue factory. What I'm saying to you, Rose, is that the publishers are on my back like monkeys and the printer is sitting with his finger on the big button. I'm under the most awful pressure, Rose. I feel like Agatha Christie at a pub quiz. I'd love to put our emails in the book, Rose. I think they'd really bring something to the party. What do you think? Come on, Rose, get involved. You owe it to yourself.

Bob

From: Rose
To: Bob Servant Subject: RE: 'Why Me?'

NO

From: Bob Servant
To: Rose
Subject: re: 'Why Me?'

Rose,

That's fine. I have too much respect for you to ask again.

Your Servant,
Bob Servant

NO REPLY

Dear Bob,

A few years ago, I loaned you the deposit to stand for election as an independent candidate for our hometown of Broughty Ferry. The money had been saved to provide me with a new bathroom suite. History shows that the deposit was lost. Is there any chance whatsoever of me seeing the money again? As you are aware, I had already removed my previous bathroom. Living without a bathroom is an enormous challenge, hence my question to you today.

Yours in distress,
Frank, Broughty Ferry, Dundee

* * * * *

Frank,

As I've told you many times, that deposit was a small price to pay for the important life lesson of 'don't be hasty'. With regards to your self-inflicted toilet situation, you live less than 300 metres from the bowling club and only have to climb over two walls to get there. If you fail to make that journey without incident then that is a nutritional issue for which I cannot be reasonably asked to take responsibility.

Yours in Thanks,
Bob

Hi Bob,

You're not getting any younger. As a lawyer I was wondering if you've written your will?

Derek Stillie, Ayrshire

* * * * *

Dear Derek,

I have.

Yours in hope,
Bob

'He Left 'Em Wanting More'

The Last Will and Tenement
of Robert Servant

- -

I leave my extension to the good people of Broughty
Ferry. In return, the anniversary of my death will be
known forever as 'Bob Fest'. Every man, woman and
child will dress up as me in a bunnet and moustache
and murals of me will be proudly displayed around
Broughty Ferry. If anyone draws testicles dangling
from my ears like testicle earrings or from my chin as
a testicle beard then they will be sent to prison.

I leave my One-Finger Lettuce Shredder invention to my
paperboy, Darren. He's ready.

I leave my collection of aprons to the Dundee Museum
of Art for them to use in a major exhibition entitled
"All Down His Front — The Life, Times and Aprons of
Robert Servant".

I leave my Andy Murray nickname, "The Dunblane Hydro",
to the nation.

I leave my trampoline to the Fire Brigade for use in
rescue missions and not as a toy.

I leave the following to my friend and right-hand-man
Frank — the burger van and all fittings, permission to
use all of my jokes to the best of his ability, my
You've Been Framed back catalogue on VHS, the
cardboard box under my stairs marked 'Don't Look And
Even If You Do This Stuff Isn't Mine It Came With The
House', my jumper and cardigan collection, the static
caravan, £18.72 credit at Zapzone and the saying
"onions for show, burgers for dough".

Dear "Bob",

You're getting older and this kind of thing has been going on for quite a long time. When exactly are you planning to stop?

Stewart and Joan F, Broughty Ferry

* * * * *

Dear Stewart and Joan,

Thanks for your support over the years, I am sure you will be delighted to hear that things are starting to wrap up,

Yours in gratitude,

Bob

~~~~~~~~~~

La comédie est terminée

Servant Retires (Again)

Broughty Ferry businessman Bob Servant has called time on the reprisal of his burger-van empire, saying he wants more time to 'dream big and watch the telly'. Servant originally hung up his apron in the wake of Dundee's Cheeseburger Wars in the eighties before making what he termed his 'Second Coming' last year.

'Frank Sinatra'

'The punters wanted us back and we delivered,' said Servant. 'Now it's time for me to take a step back and consider my next move.' 'People say that I've made more comebacks than Frank Sinatra,' joked Servant, who was unable to clarify who the aforementioned 'people' are. 'I'm not one to brag,' he added, 'but I'm a great guy.'

'Outer Space'

'When I look back on my life,' said Servant, 'I see some of the greatest glories imaginable. The longest window-cleaning round in western Europe and a burger-van collection that, at its peak, could be seen from outer space. More skirt than I have known what to do with, and thousands upon thousands of happy punters. The fact that I have managed to stay humble is perhaps my greatest achievement of all.'

Servant's denied his decision to close his burger van is connected to 18 outstanding Health and Safety writs, which he described as '18 storms in 18 teacups'.

Bob,

You're going to die soon. Any last thoughts?

Michael Berkeley, Toronto

* * * * *

Michael,

Thanks for your encouraging message. As it happens, I have recently found myself considering my life, and reflecting upon what I've learnt along the way.

Biggest regret? Losing my only VHS copy of Bus Conductresses Gone Wild on the Waltzers at Broughty Ferry Gala Week in 1987. It dropped into the machinery and was smashed to smithereens. To this day I wake up screaming at the memory.

Biggest disappointment? My off-peak timeshare at the 'Adults Only' static-caravan park in Pitlochry. I critically misunderstood the nature of the Adults Only theme, with disastrous and demeaning results.

Finally, the question people ask me the most is for the secret of life. The more life I live, the more I realise that it's all about your walk. My walk is essentially a jazz piece. There's no real structure to it and no two performances are exactly the same. I've picked up influences everywhere from traditional marching bands to nature documentaries, and the result is astonishing. Get yourself a good walk, my friends, and you'll get yourselves a good life.

Yours,
Bob

A big "Cheerio" from Bob Servant

Well, here we are. Nearly done and the fat lady's about to swing[45]. I don't mind telling you that I'm bloody knackered after knocking out one last book. No wonder the woman from *Murder She Wrote* looks so old. I feel like my brain has been pickled by a top chef and that my heart has been inflated with a foot pump by Russell Grant.

Thanks for reading. Unless you're standing holding it in the book shop, in which case you're an absolute disgrace.

Your Servant,
Bob Servant.

---

[45] Sing, hopefully

Acknowledgments by Neil Forsyth

My grateful thanks to Stephen Simpson and all at Winter and Simpson printers in Dundee for their invaluable help and generous support in the printing of this book, along with Ann McHattie at Barr Printers. Thank you to the Broughty Ferry Bookhouse, who have very generously waived all commission on sales of this book, as well as all other bookshops who have taken it. Thank you also to everyone who has bought the book and helped support the amazing work of the Dundee Bairns charity, who will receive all proceeds from this book. I'm grateful to the brilliant Pete McKee for generously allowing me to use his magnificent Bob Servant artwork on the front cover. My grateful thanks to Rhiannon for editing this book and maintaining sanity while doing so. And now, I suppose, to Bob.

I found him sitting in Broughty Ferry's celebrated Stewpot's bar, engrossed in the letters page of the Dundee Evening Telegraph. Bob placed the newspaper down, tapped his finger on the letters page and said with a wink that it was 'a good argument for laboratories'. Over the following, uncomfortable half an hour, which included an emotional ten-minute conversation where I coaxed Bob back out of a toilet cubicle, it emerged that he had intended to say 'lobotomies'.

I suggested a walk along Broughty Ferry's Brook Street, a road Bob refers to as 'The Walk of Fame'. As we walked, Bob told me an approaching woman was 'not so much an old flame, more of an old inferno'. The woman walked past without any sign of recognition. Bob said she was obviously 'still hurting' and 'a prisoner of the past'. An elderly member of the clergy saw Bob approach and jogged away. Bob saw a man in a café, aggressively cajoled him out to the street, and pointed out how much the man resembled the television presenter Des Lynam. The man angrily wrestled himself free from Bob and returned to his befuddled wife. Bob, his palms raised in despair, told me 'this is what I'm up against'.

I mentioned that Broughty Ferry has a joie de vivre. Bob says it doesn't, but there's a Caffé Nero. He made us cross the road to avoid three woman pushing infant children in prams. He called them a 'hen party' and revealed his fear they would try and 'touch me up'. Bob started to speculate where on his body their attack would 'inevitably concentrate…'

'Shall we go down to the river?' I intervened.

The harbour at Broughty Ferry offers a sweeping view of the surroundings and I asked Bob about his unbreakable attachment with the area. 'This used to be my playground,' he said simply. It was a whimsical touch that I enjoyed until noticing he was pointing at a children's playground over the road. I asked if he had ever considered leaving the area. Bob told me about a promotion in the Dundee Courier in the late 1980s. Bob collected thirteen daily tokens in a row for a coach trip to the Lake District. Tragically, on the 14th and final day of the promotion Bob did not buy a copy of the newspaper ('Frank's fault, let's leave it at that') and therefore missed out on the coach trip. 'Little twists' said Bob in conclusion. He acted out a twisting action that mutated into the mimed opening of a wine bottle, followed by the mimed pouring and drinking of a glass of wine. Concerned that Bob was planning to drink the whole virtual bottle, I suggested that I walk him home.

As we walked, I asked Bob if he wanted to thank anyone in the Acknowledgements section. 'Andre Agassi,' shrugged Bob, 'for showing me that it could be done.' When we passed Frank's house Bob coughed and said that I 'might as well' add in the Acknowledgements that Frank is 'all right'. I observed that Frank's great strength is his loyalty and Bob nodded in agreement. 'He's my Ginger Roger,' he said. 'Ginger Rogers,' I corrected. 'No, Ginger Roger,' confirmed Bob, clarifying that he referred to a red-haired man from Lochee who is locally accepted as being especially loyal.

Back at Bob's, we sat together in deckchairs in his front garden. Broughty Ferry was catching the last of the evening sun, which dipped into the river beyond the Tay Bridge. I found myself thinking about Bob. About an all the years we've spent connected, and now there was to be a farewell. I could tell from Bob's demeanour that he was thinking the same. How might we effectively capture what this moment meant? As Dundonian men, we lacked the tools for such emotional exchanges. I decided to help us both. I stood and said, simply but loaded with subtext, 'I'm going now.'

Bob turned to me. 'I'd genuinely forgotten,' he said, 'that you were here.'

Neil Forsyth